Franklin Boggs
from
Lesh Jr.
Xmas 24

A small boat was in a few minutes rocking alongside of the seaplane. Page 46.

"Our Young Aeroplane Scouts Fighting to a Finish."

Our Young Aeroplane Scouts

Fighting To The Finish

OR

Striking Hard Over The Sea For
The Stars And Stripes

By HORACE PORTER

AUTHOR OF

"Our Young Aeroplane Scout Series"

A. L. BURT COMPANY
NEW YORK

OUR YOUNG AEROPLANE SCOUTS

(Registered in the United States Patent Office)

A Series of Remarkable Stories of the Adventures of
Two Boy Flyers in the European War Zone

By HORACE PORTER

Copyright, 1918
By A. L. BURT COMPANY

OUR YOUNG AEROPLANE SCOUTS FIGHTING
TO THE FINISH

OUR YOUNG
AEROPLANE SCOUTS

CHAPTER I

WALKED INTO A TRAP

In an old French house in Rouen, close by the river Seine, a quaint and ancient structure, "full of gusts of wind, of ghosts and twisted passages," as its early history went, Gilbert LeFane, the premier aviator of France, indulged this winter night in one of his restless rests, awaiting, with hardly concealed impatience, the arrival of a something or somebody, about which or whom the great and gallant airman was certainly manifesting a high degree of personal interest.

Pacing at short lengths a widely shining floor path, the reflection of a glowing back-log behind the hearth of an immense fireplace, the kingpin of flyers for the Tricolor time and again addressed the half-

3

dozing occupant of a spacious and easy chair in the chimney-corner, a gray-topped, spare figure, nursing a huge meerschaum, in lean fingers, every remark of the famous high rider bearing upon one subject:

"Time enough, Monsieur Coursey, for steam to bring anyone twice the distance that lies between here and Havre. Everything seems tied fast to the ground this night."

"My good Gilbert," chuckled the elder in the easy chair, "you figure too much on aeroplane time. People on earth are no meteors like you men who ride on wings. Hold your peace and save your steps."

"My good Gilbert" was not influenced by this advice to "save your steps;" indeed, he extended them beyond the red fire line for a gaze out of one of the front windows, overlooking the narrow street.

"If these doctors," he muttered, beating tattoo on a window pane, "attempt to keep me much longer like a caged bear, I'll start a riot—and what's more, if those boys don't show up pretty soon, I'll jump out of my skin."

LeFane and an aviator companion had a week or two previously been for three days and nights the sport of wild winds and waves, when a German

Gotha with hot shot dropped the seaplane in which they were riding upon the turbulent surface of the North Sea, an exhausting experience in the wrecked cruiser serving to force into the temporary invalid list even so hardy and well seasoned a pair as Gilbert and his comrade.

"Those boys" of muttering mention were the leaders in a remarkable rescue of the sorely imperiled aviators, and aboard a mammoth hydroplane in accomplishing the wonderful find on a wide waste of water.

The young heroes of this life-saving venture were the expected guests of the deeply grateful Frenchman so eagerly anticipating the arrival of a couple whose aerial feats of daring so nearly rivalled his own.

A sound of voices in the street outside, a crisping of the hard-packed snow under foot, and a thump at the front entrance of the old house. Before LeFane could complete a turn from the window, Monsieur Coursey, with surprising alacrity, had hastened to respond to the summons of the knocker.

When the massive door creaked open, two fine-looking young fellows, buttoned close in leather jackets, put their heads in, looking round with expectant manner for the one they most desired to see, but not neglecting to bid a pleasant good evening to the little gray man who gave them first greeting.

At sight of LeFane, however, the salutation of the incoming lads took a more boisterous turn, threatening to raise the echoes supposed to be lingering in the darker recesses of the ancient structure that their friend Gilbert called home.

"How goes it, bold mariner?" almost shouted the stouter-built youth of the visiting pair, seizing the extended hand of his eminent exponent of the flying game, who heartily replied to the question fired at him:

"Marked sound by everybody except a couple of army medics, and even that mark wearing off. How's the Barry and Trouville twins?"

"Feeling like the partition of a stove—great," gaily assured the husky youngster, stepping aside to give his pal a chance to exercise a hand grip upon the willing host.

The illumination of the fire and lamp-lit room revealed the presence of Billy Barry, Bangor, Maine, U. S. A., and his inseparable comrade, Henri Trouville, a thoroughly Americanized native of France, known, in "double harness," wherever world warring flags were carried, as the Young Aeroplane Scouts.

Within a week past the Bangor boy had qualified, in a London lawyer's office, as one of the two heirs of a millionaire uncle in the "land of the free," a fortune that owed considerable of its bulk to the manufacture of flying machines.

"To whoop up the cause of the Allies," as Billy explained it, "this brother of the wings and myself are bound for the country and the state where the spruce comes from, with the full intent of doing a bit toward filling the air spaces above the war zones with American aeroplanes. When I get my money working in the big factory at home," the young scout added, "you can safely wager that this flying firm of ours will be back for the finish, in person and as large as life."

Even now a ship was anchored in the basin at Havre, under near sailing orders, in which vessel our boys had secured passenger privilege for the return voyage to the States, after more than three years' absence—years replete with strenuous adventure and remarkable achievements for and by the aerial twins above and about the battlefields of the old world.

This night visit, then, in Rouen, was a hurried mission, and for the kindly purpose alone of bidding good-bye to the gallant flight companion for the time being withdrawn from continuous flying activity by chance misfortune.

Our Young Aeroplane Scouts had no reason to anticipate aught else at this journey's end than serving the friendly purpose mentioned, and, homebound in immediate prospect, entertained no thought of any happening that would tend to interfere with their early departure.

Had LeFane been in his usual fighting trim, and some stirring venture suddenly presenting itself, there might have been a mental combat, on the part of the scrappy young aviators, against the temptation of once more mixing in.

But the fire-eating Gilbert, with a red flannel rag around his neck and slippered feet upon the hearth, was no vision of heroic mould at 10 o'clock this winter night, when he and his comforting guests were talking over recent performance in which the trio had joined in repelling both submarine and seaplane invasion by the Huns of the English Channel and contiguous territory.

A little later, after Monsieur Coursey had happily officiated at the serving of a supper, which left nothing to be desired, the young scouts regretfully advised that they must be on their way back to Havre within the next half hour.

"Make it to-morrow," pleaded LeFane. "It's a short go, and time enough, I'm sure, to catch your boat."

"Sorry, old man," replied Billy, "but we can't take any more risks of missing our one chance in a month of getting across the big pond. The boss of the ark gave us fair warning to 'stick around' close enough to hear the starting bell, and we're out of bounds now just for the pleasure of an hour or two in your company. Good luck to you, good friend, we are holding the big hope that soon we will meet again."

Gilbert, realizing that further urging was useless, wrung the hands of the leaving lads, to whom he owed his life, and with Monsieur Coursey stood at the window that he might exchange a last gesture of farewell with the youths as they passed under the street lamp outside.

"We'll have to hustle to get the train, Buddy," announced the Bangor boy, who had been inspecting his watch, and setting a lively pace for his pal to keep on even footing.

Owing to the bite of the weather, and the time of night, the narrow thoroughfare the young scouts were traversing was practically deserted, save for themselves, but they had no reckoning of interference with their progress in the capital of the department of Seine-Inferieure, or any need of gendarmes to back up their own ready wits and stout arms in case of necessity.

A running crossfire of talk about their prospective voyage, how it would feel to once more view the Statue of Liberty, of the happy sensation of walking into the aeroplane factory as they used to do when the morning whistle sounded—all this diversion rendered the boys wholly oblivious of surroundings, and, naturally, not at all alert to the fact that on the opposite side of the street they were being stealthily stalked by a pair of soft-stepping, shadowy figures, while a short distance further ahead, where the extended roofs of two old-time structures almost met and created a canopy of darkness, there was more of lurking menace to the light-hearted aviators hastening trainward.

However, just as the young scouts were setting their strides into the forbidding passage in front, the Bangor boy was suddenly possessed with one of those instinctive promptings of threatened danger, which many a time and oft had served him well in other tight places, and where the shuffle for good or ill was a mighty close proposition.

With a restraining arm across the breast of his comrade, young Barry halted in his tracks, his free hand resting on his hip, where reposed an up-to-date, many-speaking "gun," while his keen eyes peered into the forward blackness.

Henri, instantly keyed up to the situation, and far too wary a campaigner to give voice to question, similarly sought his revolver pocket, ready for any emergency.

The brief relaxing from fixed habit of alertness, though, induced by unusual change of thought and the environments of a supposed safety zone, worked in advance to the present undoing of two of the sharpest "blades" in the air-cutting business.

As Billy was wont to remark, "If we're ever weasels asleep, it's on the ground we are"—a little bit of Irish finish, and intended modest acknowledgment of the best hold of Our Young Aeroplane Scouts being aloft rather than below, that seemed to fit the unforeseen situation against which they had just stumbled.

Neither of the boys was given a chance to finger a trigger nor, indeed, to even lift a hand in defense against the intangible something of dread that the Maine lad, staring forward, had unaccountably fixed in his mind's eye.

From the rear, silently stealing forms, like a flash materialized with catapult force of attack, and the young aviators were instantly and stiflingly enveloped, from head to foot, in the folds of some heavy wollen fabric, and with the further suffocating accompaniment of throttling embrace about the neck, an encircling by steel-muscled arms that effectually prevented outcry on the part of the victims of the cunningly planned assault.

As swiftly and noiselessly as was accomplished the "bagging" of the young scouts were the cloth bundles containing them, carried, or dragged, through the doorway of one of the nearby houses, with never a window light showing and so located that the street lamps failed to throw even a pencil line of illumination on the somber front.

Once inside, and the entrance door soundlessly closed and bolted, Billy and Henri were afforded the welcome relief of again breathing freely, by the prompt removal of the swathings in which they had been so closely trussed.

"What's the idea?" was the characteristic query of the Bangor boy in the very first second after he got a good lungful of air.

Still in darkness, the boy could not discern any particular captor at which to aim his question, but he "felt" the presence of presumably several, who might answer if they so desired.

"I say," repeated the young scout, in louder tone, when there was continued lack of response, "what are you fellows driving at? Just a plain hold-up, is it, or, if not that, give it a name."

"If you don't curb your tongue," sternly advised a husky voice in the protesting lad's ear, "you'll get a knuckle on your windpipe."

"I tell you," persisted Billy, "that this thing is getting tiresome. Show a hand, can't you?"

The "hand" of which the meddlesome lad was demanding sight was presented in the shape of a severely pinching grip around the wrist, and another menacing whisper conveying peremptory advice:

"Shut up!"

While his pal was endeavoring to work up a bluff of some sort, Henri had made the disappointing discovery that his pistol pocket was empty, and no opportunity of making a worth-while strike for liberty or, at least, creating an alarm by the explosion of a cartridge. Billy had had the same baffling experience a minute or two previously.

The latter youth, now realizing that any line of talk he might conceive was not likely to have any beneficial effect for the present, accepted the admonition, impressed by painful pressure, and "shut up" like a clam.

So it was a wordless movement that next followed, when the captives, pushed and pulled, set foot on an ascending stairway, faintly illumined by the small glowing tip of an electric pocket flash carried by the self-constituted leader of the climbers.

At the top of the flight, and at the end of a long and exceedingly narrow passage, a quickly opened door revealed light, all sufficient for the boys to size up the party who had them in tow.

The chief object of interest, though, it immediately developed, was the waiting individual in the room into which the young scouts were ushered.

CHAPTER II

A BID OF DEFIANCE

THE very picture of the bluff and hearty skipper of some river-plying boat, one of the artful make-ups for which the wonderful camouflager was re-nowned, the greeting occupant of the dingy apart-ment of dusty floors and smoke-discolored walls would have succeeded, and, no doubt, did, in mak-ing the counterfeit just about the genuine thing in any port of call on shore or coast.

But here were two viewers of the masked pres-ence, so unceremoniously brought face to face with the foxy masquerader, who could not be fooled for more than a minute as to the real identity of the posing sailor. They had seen the same man as mer-chant, doctor, tourist, innocent bystander, and other rôles too numerous to remember, when, in and out of the German empire, these witnesses were, for compelling reasons, intimately attached to the lead-ing strings of the "smooth" personage.

Billy Barry and Henri Trouville no sooner looked into the eyes of their chief captor—as keen as gimlet points—than they had the name "Roque" on the tips of their tongues.

Roque, the noted secret agent of Kaiserland, the master hand that manipulated a thousand unseen wires, controlling and animating everywhere the silent workers, who adroitly served their cause behind the veil of intrigue.

The knowledge of the young scouts in relation to this man, if heralded outside the walls which now held them prisoners, would have resulted in a mighty short shrift for the eminent schemer and his henchmen holding sway this night in the ramshackle structure on a side street of Rouen.

With the sight and recognition of the directing figure of the "bagging" performance, which had brought himself and flying partner to grief, the Bangor boy was speedily relieved of any relief that the motive of the night attack had behind it the discovery by somebody that he was a newly created millionaire, and, therefore, a sizable hostage for ransom, or, again, that the hold-up was merely an Apache conception of stripping a couple of wayfarers of their valuables.

"A pleasure, indeed," began the pseudo sailor, when the boys received another push forward by the men behind them, "and just like old times."

"Some old buncombe," thought Billy, "the tiger with his claws under the velvet."

But aloud the lad replied: "After small game to-night, it seems, Herr Roque. We are sure honored by your attention."

The thin lips of the secret agent developed a grim smile at the address of the youth before him.

"You have been in bad company recently, young sirs," he remarked, "and are in need, I think, of a reforming influence."

The flying twins quickly realized that this reference had to do with their recent association with Ardelle, who, for France and her Allies, was in counterpart rôle to that of this astute underground worker for the German empire, the two putting up a strong case of "diamond cut diamond" ever since the war broke out.

In their last previous clash of wits, Roque had received the worst of it, and Our Young Aeroplane Scouts had played a considerable part in putting a quietus on the deep-laid scheme of the Teuton plotter to work havoc by means of a submarine raid in the English Channel.

Labeled, then, as too active factors in kicking a hole in one of Roque's carefully spun webs, the boys had created the incentive and unwittingly furnished the opportunity for the arch-plotter to pounce upon them.

Hardly a doubt could be entertained but that the home of LeFane had been a point of watching on the part of the slyly operating outfit which had "nipped" Billy and Henri after their visit to the ailing aviator, the latter, on his own account, being a special object of attention as an able aid of Ardelle in the recent baffling of Roque, and, too, always a danger mark when the Huns essayed aerial invasion.

Indeed, from later conversation overheard by the young scouts, among the conspirators who held them captive, the youths were convinced that the great French aviator needed warning, which they would have given a good deal at the moment to convey.

Having been eliminated for a little time from direct inspection during consultation between the chief and his present serving company, the boys indulged in some looking over on their own hook, taking the measure of the assembly to whom they would have so gladly said farewell.

Barring the central figure, though, not one among the half-dozen others in the dingy room did the lads recollect of ever having seen before in the immediate service of Roque, when they were sometimes observers of the movements of the secret agent in the long ago.

One fact, however, was particularly impressed upon the young aviators, that every man present would be a difficult person to tackle in physical combat, unless behind a "gun" pulled and used quicker than the other fellow could do it.

And, further, the whole "bunch" of brawn and sinew stood between the prisoners and the only door in the room. As for the windows, they were heavily shuttered tighter than wax.

So much for the situation as they then sized it up, leaving the boys in an apparently hopeless thinking part, leaning against one of the smoke-be-grimed walls of the apartment in which they were caged.

"Good-bye, ship," was Billy's whispered lament to his pal, under cover of a louder trend of the conversation engaging Roque and his companions.

"All up with that booking," softly assented Henri, with a disconsolate shrug of the shoulders.

They were then aware that Roque was again eyeing them, and very likely a contemplation which meant the fixing of their fate, of which, under the circumstances, the steady gazer might well claim to be the arbiter.

Tapping the palm of one hand with the fingers of the other, a Roque habit in advance of some expressed decision, which the boys readily recalled, the secret service chief, dropping the manner of his assumed character and the real man showing, approached the prisoners with measured step.

When closely face to face with the aviators, he sternly addressed them:

"What I ought to do with you, I suppose, would be to act upon the verdict of my men, an ugly thing to contemplate, I assure you, but, with certain memories of the past, it goes against the grain with me to reconcile myself to such an extreme measure, as proposed. I cannot offer you liberty; yet, perhaps, the more precious thing, life itself, is in my promise if you do my bidding. One of you, and the choice is yours, shall proceed to Havre to-morrow with a member of my company as a companion, who will arrange for the taking of your belongings aboard the vessel upon which you expected to sail for the United States. This accomplished, you will find it convenient to further extend your shore leave for an hour or two, plenty of time to visit with your obliging 'friend' a neat little craft anchored in the Seine. That is all, except that I will soon again be your host, and rejoice in the reunion of the one who goes and the one who stays."

The boys had their eyes fixed on Roque during every second of the time it took him to submit the startling proposition, amazed at the knowledge of their plans possessed by the speaker, and intensely curious to know at just what the man was driving.

Sparring for time to collect his wits, Billy remarked, with a forced smile:

"But, Herr Roque, our baggage, such as it is, is already aboard the ship."

"Oh, as for that," laughed the secret agent, assuming an off-hand manner, "just an extra satchel will do, which I will provide, only as a sort of passport to permit my curious friend, and yours for the time being, to see the inside of a big liner."

Henri gave his pal the foot nudge. The boys, now keyed up to the situation, at once comprehended as one the fell purpose of the arch-schemer. That "extra luggage" would more than likely contain something decidedly unusual in a plain traveler's outfit—something, at a fixed time, which would rend and wreck anything afloat except, perhaps, an iron-clad.

A question now by the Trouville lad:

"Are you not, sir, reposing considerable faith in your continued control over Billy or me, whichever is designated to be turned loose on such an errand? What's to prevent"—another query—"the one or the other of us freed, from landing the whole bunch of you where you belong?"

"Have you lost your reckoning of me so soon?" countered Roque. "Why"—this in incisive and tense tones—"if such a thing as you last mentioned should happen; if I should fail to meet the absent one of the pair of you in company with my man at a given place by sundown to-morrow, the hostage I retain will cease to live before night is well settled. All that your turn-coating could, anyhow, do would be to start a chase after nothing here. My revenge is sure. Well, is the original offer, as it stands, worth the price of both your lives?"

"It isn't worth shucks, as far as our action in it

is concerned," declared the Bangor boy, now at white heat. "You can do your worst to us, if that's your judgment, for, point-blank, and no change, I say 'No' to what you propose!"

"Same here," was Henri's emphatic put in.

Roque wore his most ominous frown, and the set of his square jaw indicated the temperature of the wrath he was nursing within.

He had made a catchless cast in deep water, and well he knew it, but so illy did he accept of anything that ran contrary to his iron will that it meant a mighty unpleasant period ahead for the defiant young scouts.

"Here, Fred," he peremptorily commanded, turning to a six-footer with a bullet-head and a suit of hair like a yellow mane on top of it, "give these lords of creation a berth with the rats. The less they sleep the more they'll think before morning."

"Fred" was prompt in gripping the elbows of the youths sentenced to a bad night in the cellar region of the old-time structure, and started with them toward the winding stairway that led from the upper hall into the darksome depths below. Another of the secret service contingent—getting signal to assist from the ireful chief—hastened to precede the departing trio with the guiding rays of an electric torch.

At the first landing of the staircase, in descent, the movers downward were suddenly halted by a tapping at the street door of the house. The man with the electric glim quickly shut off its illumination and listened attentively, standing like a statue, for a repetition of the soft knocking. The individual having Billy and Henri in close custody had instantly produced from within his blouse a something to remind the boys that silence was their warrant of safety—impressed in the darkness by the touch of cold steel on their hands.

Tap, tap, tap,—tap—three short ones, a second or two lapse for the fourth. The tip of the "glitter stick" again cast its glow, fixed upon the bolt that held the door from the inside, which was quickly shot back when the knuckle signal proved satisfactory, admitting a short, thick-set man, muffled to the ears in a greatcoat of the cabman variety.

"What's up?" gruffly questioned the bullet-headed custodian of the young scouts, with the care, however, of low pitch, speaking in the language prevailing over the Rhine.

"Paris got a bombing this evening," exulted the

newcomer, but with the same restraint of sound, "and done neatly from above by our aircraft. That flying Frenchman up the street, said to be a sick devil or devilish sick, didn't look like it to me a little while ago when he charged through the town like a mad bull on the way to the aerodrome. He had just heard, I guess, of what had happened in his beloved capital."

The speaker added a chuckle to the last observation, but quiet at that, for an upward glance by him caught the living picture of his feared chief, framed in the doorway above and outlined by a light shining from the room in the rear.

The eager informant made a bee-line upstairs, while the boys and their guards proceeded in lowering trend to the cellar. A rasp of rusty hinges, an outrush of damp air, and the young aviators were introduced to the dismal enclosure, where they were supposed to await for several weary, dreary hours final disposition at the hands of the implacable Roque.

However, the mentioned adamant chief must have thawed a little in the interim, for a messenger came down from the upper room before the lads were shut up in the underground prison to which they had just been sentenced. The emissary from above carried a couple of heavy blankets over his arm, and, after a whispered conference, the fellow with the electric illuminant surprised Billy by putting him in possession of the "glim," gruffly remarking as an accompaniment of the wholly unexpected concession:

"You're a lucky pup to get both light and covering this night. The chief surely must be threatened with heart disease."

It was noticeable that the maker of the comment apprehensively looked over his shoulder, in fear, no doubt, that "the chief" himself might be pussyfooting somewhere in the vicinity.

A shove between the shoulders hastened the ingress of the young scouts into the gloomy place of detention, and when the heavy door closed behind them it was seemingly akin to the shutting out of all hope in relation to that joyfully anticipated voyage to the U. S. A.

Billy Barry and Henri Trouville, however, were prone to rally in pinches of all sorts, and in the present grip of misfortune they did not devote many minutes to repining. The Bangor boy had already, with the aid of the flash stick, begun to take stock of the surroundings, an unevenly flagged floor, four solidly bricked walls and heavy oak beams overhead.

As the first intimation of a change of luck, the predicted rat attack did not immediately material- ize, which induced Billy to express the opinion that "all the rodents must be visiting with their kind upstairs."

Making the rounds of the improvised dungeon, Henri "barked his shins" by stumbling over a sec- tion of drain pipe which had escaped its rusted wall-pinning, and, as chance would have it, this forward precipitation brought the boy's hands, out- stretched as a protective measure, in contact with a surface point that was not brick—a grating, indeed, that guarded some outlet of the cellar enclosure—a grating with a shake to it!

"Tip us the shine here, Buddy," excitedly re- quested young Trouville. "I believe I've hit some- thing worth while."

"Buddy" did not linger in his tracks with the called-for light, and in a couple of long steps joined the discoverer of the "something worth while."

The revelation of the glowing point was such that

the Maine lad could scarcely subdue an uprising inclination to indulge in a clog-step that had almost
made him famous in a one-time amateur minstrel
show.

"It's a way to the clear, pal," he exclaimed, "if
we can only clear the way!"

CHAPTER III

AN AVIATOR'S TIMELY THOUGHT

"BLESS your awkward legs," delightedly continued the boy from Maine, edging past his pal to try a pulling experiment on the rust-eaten bars.

"Thank you for those kind words," muttered Henri, ruefully rubbing his sore knees, forgetting the pain in the next instant when Billy succeeded by the very first yank in dislodging the upper hold of the grate in the wall.

The combined strength of the boys, then applied with great zeal and determination, caused not only a shower of brick and mortar dust but with it the jingling fall of the barrier on the stone floor.

Billy flashed the electric rays here and there to ascerta. the extent of the opening created in the wall, while the other flying twin tiptoed to the cellar door with ears acute for any sound outside or just above, which would indicate whether the noise of the wrecking operation had reached the hearing of any prowling member of Roque's crew.

All was now silent as the grave and Henri rejoined his comrade at the aperture through which they hoped to accomplish a getaway.

The Bangor boy made the first squirm through the air shaft, or whatever it was supposed to be, with the glow point ahead of him, for cautious avoiding of any bump that might await at the dropping-out place.

What he really found at finish of the short crawl was a narrow passage between the house he was leaving and another similar structure opposite. Looking upward between the almost joining roof extensions, there was yet sufficient space to show a bit of star-studded sky and the lifting luminous haze of the city night lights.

Turning back the shine of the electric tip for the vision of his pal, Billy was ready with a reaching hand when Henri came through. Treading softly toward the street end of the intervening passage, the boys were halted near the exit by the dully gleaming lamps of a cab, at the sidewalk curb, the vehicle directly in front of the opening through which the lads expected to emerge—and, what's more, the cabman himself was at the very moment applying a tiny match flame to the pipe in his mouth, using the walls of the narrow outlet as a protection against the winter wind that was sweeping down the thoroughfare beyond.

With the sharp mental reminder that it was a "cabby" style of man who had brought the news of the Paris shake-up, the young scouts were not going to risk their luckily won liberty by proceeding any further front.

So they took to backtracking with due celerity and also proper regard for the way they placed their feet, in order that no sound should attract the attention of the pipe-smoking jehu.

The workout from the rear was far from inviting, a wilderness of frozen ash-heaps, snow-covered piles of tin cans and other junk and debris that made a night excursion in that direction one of many pitfalls and bruises. But the escaping youths were only too glad to tackle any sort of road that would lengthen the distance between themselves and the Roque outfit, even if it included a leap into the river.

With no idea where they were headed, the boys plunged blindly onward until they found themselves in the dock region of the town, for the time being deserted of human kind, but showing numerous welcome lights along the way.

It was just about dawn when the boys encountered a sleepy gendarme, convinced him that they were friends of LeFane, one of the celebrities of the locality, and received advices as to the next outgoing train—three hours or more hence.

"It's back to Gilbert, I guess," suggested Henri, "if he hasn't already flown the coop for Paris."

"Nothing else to do," agreed Billy, "if the policeman will map us the most direct route from here."

The "policeman" continued to be obliging, but the boys were particular in selecting the direction that did not include the vicinity of the Roque rendezvous.

They wanted to get to LeFane first, if possible, and secure his aid in successfully drawing the net around the members of the dangerous gang which were secretly housed in the very heart of Rouen.

The dock watchman to whom they had been talking was hardly up to the task of quickly organizing an effective raid, and anyways sure capture of the wily and resourceful enemy invaders. A single blunder and Roque's vanishing habit would triumph, as usual. The young scouts well knew, of old, of the disappearing necromancy exercised at will by the "fox of Berlin."

Once again on the way to the home of Gilbert, Billy and Henri scudded through the silent streets as fast as their legs would carry them, and prepared to set up a yell that would raise the dead in the event of an attempt to intercept them by any skulker under command of Roque, who might yet be on watch in the vicinity of the LeFane residence.

It was a regular thundering knock the racing youths this time applied to the front door of the ancient domicile, which brought Monsieur Coursey shuffling from a warm bed to querulously demand:

"Who's there?"

"Open, Monsieur, quick!"

This was the call of Henri, with his lips at the keyhole.

The old man evidently recognized the voice, or realized some great emergency, for the listeners outside heard immediately the drawing of a bolt from its socket, and directly got an eye-dazzling from the lamp which the lately awakened sleeper was holding high overhead.

In a brace of seconds the panting youths were under cover, and the Bangor boy demanding to know the whereabouts of their aviator friend.

"Where's his nobs?" was the form of Billy's first point-blank query.

"Off to Paris these five hours," replied Monsieur Coursey; "a messenger came with news that set Gilbert in a tiger's rage; he could not be restrained, and needs be the telegram bearer and myself aided him in his frantic haste to dress for a night flight. Merci, how the always good man did drive us with tongue lashings."

Even though the speaker gave this information at the highest speed of excitable indulgence in his native tongue, the Bangor boy was irritably impatient at the waste of words after the first sentence.

He and his flying partner need not be told the method which Gilbert, in such an emergency, would utilize in covering the air-line trifle of sixty-seven miles. That their friend had gone was the disappointing discovery in a nutshell.

"It's up to us entirely, then," declared Billy, "to kick up the hornets' nest around the hiding place of that gang down the street. Come on, Buddy, and let's stir up the town."

The gray light of morning was faintly showing when the boys made a break through the door, which the rather aggrieved Coursey had not even time to shut.

But, wonder of wonders, the lads were hardly fifty yards from the house when they ran plump into the arms of LeFane himself, the pallor of illness in his face replaced by the ruddy glow imparted by exposure to frigid blasts which the great aviator had been breasting in high altitudes and at lightning speed.

It would have been a difficult matter to establish between the three the claim of the highest degree of astonishment in regard to this unexpected meeting. LeFane had supposed, of course, that Billy and Henri were safe and snug in Havre, and Billy and Henri, on the strength of what they had just learned, had, naturally, figured Gilbert at the head of a Gotha-repelling force over the capital.

Of the trio, however, the boys had a little the best of it, by having had considerably the worst of it during the past night; in other words, the young scouts, by their changed appearance alone, commanded first interrogation as to cause and effect.

"What under the sun, moon and stars," demanded the Rouen flyer, "have you fellows been up to?"

The violent shrouding; pulling and hauling; cellar experiences; crawling through a deeply dusty airshaft; wading through ash-heaps and various products of canneries, had each and all left their marks upon the trim youths to whom Gilbert had so recently said good-bye.

Billy told the questioner all about it, talking like a mill-race runs, but even then the story had to be completed while chasing Gilbert on the way to apprize both civil and military authorities of the presence in the city of a dangerous, desperate and cunning coterie of alien conspirators.

Within half an hour the old house where Billy and Henri had been held captive was heavily guarded, front and back, while searching parties forced the doors and swarmed all over the interior. Of the former occupants there was no a trace. Indeed, until the boys offered an exhibit of the broken grating in the cellar and demonstrated their manner of escape from the premises, they were under

suspicion of being sensation mongers without any
warrant whatever. The afforded illustration of
fact, though, coupled with the indorsement of
LeFane, finally prevailed as sufficient to establish
credence for the story.

The wires were set to working in every direction,
swift craft put in operation ap und down the river,
railroad stations rigidly watched and a thorough
scouring of the city ordered.

As to the ownership of the premises involved, it
developed that one Herr Boschman had four years
previously bought this property and the house ad-
joining, and since that time both structures credited
as tenantless. It is hardly necessary to state that
"Herr Boschman" had long ceased to be a resident
of Rouen.

"It beats the band," observed Billy, when, in company with Gilbert and Henri, he was leaving the
scene of fruitless search, "how that man Roque does
it—always finds a hole, and then pulls it in after
him."

"By the way," put in young Trouville, "how
about our boat? Maybe we can get aboard and
away, after all."

LeFane inspected his watch. "Ten-thirty," he

announced. "Another train at two." On second thought, the boss aviator suggested that they ascertain whether or not the liner was still in the basin at Havre.

When the answer came, Gilbert cast a look of sympathy at his young friends.

"Sailed at seven this morning," he remarked, passing the message to Billy for inspection.

"The jig's up for this particular trip, Buddy," was the Bangor boy's sad say to his pal. "But, better luck next time, old top."

"Well, my friends," invited LeFane, "come along and enjoy a bath and some clothes-brushing. Then we'll talk over the situation and see what is the next best thing to do."

On the way home Gilbert told the boys of his night flight to Paris, and too late arrival to get in action against the raiding Gothas, leaving a trail of death and destruction in their wake.

"Duvall and Monville smashed one of them," he said, "but the others got away. I'd have traded a year or two of life for a chance in that game. Illness and iller luck, though, played against me. There's a next time, however, my lads, and, mark you, I'll exact the full measure for this bad turn."

When the young scouts had "cleaned up" and once more presented a "passable front," as Billy called it, they were eager to discuss with their tried and true friend and host the most desirable and effective manner of pursuing some further opportunity of getting passage to America.

But a solution of their problem came like a bolt from the blue, and without the aid of a talkfest. The boys had hardly made the first step of descent from an upper room to the living apartment on the ground floor of the LeFane home when they heard stentorian summons from their flying friend below.

"Get a move on you, my lads," was the loud call, and when the youths hove in sight of the now excited Frenchman, the latter was strenuously proclaiming: "Dolt that I was not to think of it before!"

Directly addressing Billy and Henri, the restlessly pacing aviator continued: "You'll go over on the craft that's got you booked! We can't miss it!"

The Bangor boy and his pal stared at the speaker, as if in fear that Gilbert had developed delirium.

"Go easy, brother," the Maine lad was prompted to advise, "you'll be all right in a little while."

" 'All right' be confounded," cried LeFane, "do you think I'm rattle-brained? Why, I've just recovered my senses, not lost them! There's a seaplane on a dock not five city squares from here. I can put a hand on Cressey" (his flying partner) "in less than twenty minutes. Catch that boat? It can be done before she's even out of the Channel!"

The flying twins were electrified by the force of Gilbert's suddenly conceived plan, wholly practicable and certainly well worthy of trial.

"Bully idea, old top," was Billy's exclamation of approval, "and let's be at it like a house afire!"

Monsieur Coursey had his second viewing that morning of a hasty exit performance, LeFane in the lead and the boys sprinting at his heels. Cressey was taken into the speedy procession, after being forced to don his flying gear with all the expedition of a lightning change artist.

The emergency spur was also applied to several assistants recruited by LeFane to aid in the launching of the big hydroplane from the river brink, and in a remarkably short space of time the great mechanical bird, aloft, was following the line of the

Seine towards its mouth and the broad expanse of the Channel.

Our Young Aeroplane Scouts were content on this occasion to sit as passengers in the onrushing craft, gentlemen of leisure, indeed, and served by two such master mariners of the upper reaches as LeFane and Cressey.

Aerially sweeping now down the waterway between France and England, in the direction of the open sea, each and all of the aviation quartette were expectantly keyed up for first sight of the outgoing ship they were seeking.

CHAPTER IV

MADE UP FOR LOST TIME

THE young scouts, having nothing else to do but keep a sharp lookout for the America-bound liner, and using their far-seeing glasses with a free hand, indulged in friendly rivalry for the honor of making initial announcement of a triumphant discovery—"spotting the funnel," as the Bangor boy happily named the gazing contest.

Many and many a funnel sent up columns of black smoke as the seaplane passed, with ever-increasing speed, over the choppy surface of the Channel, but not yet the topping of the U. S. A. craft, which would expand the throat of one or the other of the flying twins in joyful outcry.

As luck would have it, the youth from Maine pulled down the laurels just at a time when he was declaring to his pal that "this binocle is surely going back on me," and about to take an eye rest. The one last look for the moment, it so happened, "hit the mark," and Henri lost his chance of scoring by about two seconds.

"There she blows!" shouted young Barry.

The boy had picked up this form of heralding a "find" from one of the numerous stories about whalers, of which he used to be a constant reader.

But it was "she" that "blowed," no doubt about that—and the Trouville lad was perfectly willing to play second fiddle on the auspicious occasion.

"Bully boy with a glass-eye!" he vociferated, planting a sounding thump between the shoulders of his companion behind the wind-screen.

LeFane, having received his cue from Billy's exhibit of lung power, immediately sent the hydroplane to lower strata, and soon drew near to where the liner was plowing the waves.

Henri had his turn in performing as a signal worker, and by the time the aerial craft made its splash in the tide the other ship was holding to its own length in the water and awaiting the desire of the aviators.

A small boat was lowered and in a few minutes was rocking alongside of the seaplane. The officer in charge instantly recognized Billy and Henri as the expected passengers who had failed to put in appearance when the liner cleared Havre, and, also, gave expression to his surprise at their novel method of mending former delay in words that may be politely construed as "I'll be switched"—only the sentence did not exactly end that way.

The boys in the meantime were hand-gripping with LeFane and Cressey, telling these good comrades over and over again of their grateful appreciation, and reiterating the intent of soon returning for the "finish."

"You're a fine pair to be talking about being in our debt," declared Gilbert, masking his emotion with bantering tone. "Look what you did for France when you beat the North Sea out of its prey!" The speaker made a bold attempt to create a laugh with this latter statement, but be it said that not even a grin was produced.

"Look alive, my young friends," the ship's officer was saying, "we must be on the way."

As the liner resumed its majestic course, the young scouts stuck to the upper deck until the hydroplane had lifted, flown and vanished in the far-away mists above the Channel.

At the captain's table that evening the young scouts learned of the ill-fated *Tuscania,* the fine big ship torpedoed by a U-boat, and the fine big fellows whose lives were in the toll taken by the submarine barbarians.

"We'll fix 'em yet," asserted the Bangor boy, aroused to a high pitch by the relation, "and I'm mighty glad now that I've got a lot of dollars that will work in the fixing."

He was reticent, though, in regard to a recent personal achievement of himself, and the partner by his side, in the showering bombs to the best advantage upon one of the Kaiser's latest improvements in the way of underwater craft.

After what they had just heard, however, the boys found added satisfaction, at least, in thinking about the quietus they had applied.

In this crossing of the Atlantic not a single periscope showed itself to the battery of glasses constantly trained seaward in every direction. Billy laughingly insisted that Henri had the U-boats "buffaloed," and the chief officer of the liner added the table jest that this "terrible Trouville" should be compelled by the naval authorities to continue service as guardian of the ship.

The youth under fire of teasing took it in good part. Maybe, though, he wondered what the captain would have said had he or his pal given the inside facts as to their recent adventure in Rouen, and how apparently close was their "call" when they defied the German secret agent, who entertained designs of planting wrecking explosives in this very ship.

Speaking of this plan of Roque's—between themselves—the lads had been curious to know how the wily one had been misled as to the time of the sailing of the vessel, so seldom, in their knowledge, did the marvellous acumen of the arch-schemer go astray.

They had the opportunity now to learn that it had been the original intent for the liner to leave Havre in the afternoon instead of the early morning, but, under military direction, and no regular schedule to be observed, it had been decided, for certain reasons, to earlier essay the passage of the Channel.

The indefinite observance of any time-table had been anticipated, however, the boys remembered, when they had been advised to "stick around" if they did not want to take chances of being "left."

But Roque, apparently, had been fooled for once in his life, anyhow. That was a happy thought for the young scouts, and certainly happier all around to everybody else on the big boat, if they had only known it.

Billy and Henri, while wholly reserving the personal equation, had, nevertheless, passed the captain a "tip" as to the proposed visit of a "blow-up" man on board the vessel, and were somewhat surprised when the official smilingly informed them that he had been so previously advised by "Mr. Ardelle."

The flying twins looked, one at the other, and disposed of the matter in their minds by a shake of the head, as much as to say, "This water is too deep for our diving."

Notwithstanding this mutual and modest concession as to being lost in such depths as those where worked the "high brows" of the secret service profession, the boys were not lax in their observance of every fellow passenger, finding it still hard to fully believe that the foxy Roque had, in this or any other instance, only "one string to his bow."

Everybody, however, listed in first and second cabin register, had, it seemed, been "vouched for," and of all the least likely to excite suspicion were two mild-mannered men with whom the young scouts came most in contact as table seat-mates and by nearness of berthing accommodations.

These individuals, eliminating their unobtrusive conduct and affable demeanor, were of opposite types as to appearance and inclination—one a "deep-dyed student of some sort or other," as Billy sized him up, careless of attire and never without a book or two under his arm, the other having the "front" of a well-chosen representative of "big business," "a walking dollar mark"—this latter description also a pronouncement of the Bangor boy.

Both had a "clean bill of health," according to the belief of the steward.

The submarine menace failing to develop, Billy and Henri, out of reach of anything in the aeroplane line, indulged for the first time in several years in the, to them, unusual pastime of doing a walk-around that led nowhere.

"Gee," remarked the Maine youth on the third day out, "this is sure a quiet life! It's funny when you can't hear a big gun, even once in a while."

"Had some experience in the field, eh?"

This query from the dapper gentleman of financial stamp, who, standing near the lads at the ship's rail, had overheard the speaker.

"Been around a little," admitted Billy. "Some noise, sir, in modern warfare."

"I suppose so," replied the genial stranger, toying with a fat, black cigar, "though I fear I cannot claim intimate acquaintance with artillery practice."

"Don't have to be too 'intimate,'" put in Henri. "You can hear them, believe me, a long ways off."

The cigar was alight now and the smoker smiling at the words of the lad. Then, turning, he acknowledged the "Good morning" salutation of the supposed "student," nursing one of his inevitable volumes.

"Nice day, gentlemen," observed the newcomer, politely bowing to the members of the little group.

"Considering that it's overcoat weather," rejoined the smoker, again displaying a double row of well-preserved teeth, "it will do finely."

With this passage of pleasantry, the bookish personage disappeared below deck for his customary "digging" in the reading room.

"Up to his ears in learning," casually commented the man with the cigar, watching the retreating figure to the vanishing point.

Somehow or other it appeared to Billy that this

seemingly careless observer had a look in his eye, an odd gleam, not theretofore noticeable.

Whether or no this impression was a freak of imagination on the part of the Bangor boy, there was nothing in the expression of the looker but kindly attention when he once more faced his young companions, and directly, with a parting wave of the hand, leaving them to their own devices.

"Mr. Augustus DeVries of Paris and London has now departed," proclaimed Henri to his pal.

"As long as you know so much," said Billy, "what's the full 'handle' of the library chap that first passed out?"

"By the same token—the steward," advised young Trouville, "he answers to the name of Albert Arthur Simmons, location, when at home, Berne, Switzerland."

"You're engaged for city directory work as soon as we land," laughed the boy from Maine.

Late that evening the boys noted "Mr. Augustus DeVries of Paris and London" emerging from the captain's official sanctum, minus his customary smile, and an added curious contraction of the eyelids.

"Lost his mask of benevolence in there," commented Billy in an undertone to his partner. "Wonder what bit him? And, do you know, Buddy," continued the boy, "something struck me this morning that that fellow had more up his sleeve than a cuff. I don't know just why, but there was that in his look for a flashlight space which set a 'hunch' to working inside me."

"That 'hunch of yours," observed Henri, "has hit the mark more than once to my knowledge, and maybe you've rung the bell again."

The Bangor boy had scored a ringer, as will be developed later.

CHAPTER V

UNMASKING OF A SPY

THE liner, making fine passage, was about a day and a half from U. S. A. port, and the after-dinner hour was on in the lounging quarters of the big vessel. Some of the passengers were devoting attention to an acrobatic pianist, others seeking cards for diversion, and here and there were sea travelers who did not seem to be doing much of anything.

In the latter list were "Mr. Augustus DeVries of Paris and London" and "Mr. Albert Arthur Simmons," hailing, by register, from Berne, Switzerland. Billy Barry and Henri Trouville, Our Young Aeroplane Scouts, as to occupation, figured for the time in the betwixt and between class, that is, they were taking it easy of body, but yet busy with their eyes, making the "mild-mannered" pair of recent acquaintance the objective points of vision. There was, at the moment, no particular reason for this steady observation, save the imagination of the lads that the before-mentioned genial mixers were of curiously changed aspect. The "student," to the viewers, wore an expression of sullen resentment, and the representative of "big business," so appearing, had a "bull-dog" set of countenance as he sat with fixed gaze on the "bookish" individual.

This transformation, in lesser degree, the boys had noticed at table shortly before, which change, even, would not have attracted their special attention, had it not been for the furtive eye demonstration of the dapper gentleman at the conclusion of the recent sociability encounter of the two strangers on the upper deck. This incident, as once before stated, had, somehow or other, oddly impressed the Bangor boy, a straw in the wind, so to speak, but yet a straw that twisted in Billy's thinking apparatus, already in tune with the haunting belief that Roque had not discarded his former practice of always having more than one iron in the fire when setting his mind upon a certain line of underworking procedure.

The Maine lad, however, was not yet counting himself as any "great shakes" at the sleuthing business, for he would then have been willing to confess that from the start neither "DeVries" nor

"Simmons" had appealed to him as worth-while objects of suspicion, or that they were other than they appeared to be, and, for all he knew even now, barring his intangible "hunch," Henri and himself were constructing mystery out of idle conjecture.

That these hail-fellow-well-met shipmates had suddenly developed a grouch apiece there was no question, but nowhere else than in ocean-going, when the going is good, is the personality of neighbors so important an asset of curiosity, and the young scouts having once struck a "lead," were really enjoying the fascinating and popular sea game of "guess."

Little, after all, they reckoned what the revelation was to be when the "incidents" they had strung together became in reality a veritable chain when welded by an adept in the high art of detection.

"Let's go over and see if we can't turn on the smile fountain again," suggested Billy, commencing to weary of silent contemplation, and referring to the pair who seemed to have lost their grip on the happy side of life.

With the approach of the lads, both "DeVries" and "Simmons" reassumed their wonted air of good-fellowship, though the last-named personage was not quite "up to snuff," as the Bangor boy later remarked to his chum, and some time before the exciting experience that enlivened the midnight hour, when the young scouts had such an awakening from sound slumber that effectually routed their oft-spoken complaint of "nothing doing on this voyage."

Quite a while in advance of the lads' retirement to their berths the "bookish" man had disappeared from the place of general assembly, and the "Paris and London" chap, betaking himself to where he could devote his entire attention to one of the fat, black cigars he cultivated, Billy and Henri, for want of something else to do, joined the chorus aids of a lively singer at the piano.

"Well, old top," yawned the Maine lad, along about 11 o'clock, "it's a witching hour for us to go and seek some dreams about Uncle Samdom, for it won't be long now before we'll be doing what the late Christopher Columbus did."

Young Trouville was ready to accept the sleep proposition without argument, but, if he, in the "land of nod," had any dreams of the "land of the free" it could not be proved by him after the unforeseen "shake-up."

The report of a pistol shot was what made the boys "sit up and take notice"—the detonation sharply sounding in the stilly night, and the next door but one to the quarters where the young scouts were so peacefully reposing.

"Gee whiz!" Billy was giving utterance to his favorite exclamation point, like a jumping-jack, springing to half-upright position in his bunk.

The other flying twin had a foot on the floor before his eyes were fairly open. In close quarters, and the lately adopted habit of a quiet life, the explosive disturbance had decidedly more effect upon the aviators as a rousing factor than a whole lot of cannonading in the field, through which latter rumbling they had often "snoozed" without the least discomfort or agitation.

"What's broke loose?" questioned Henri, while planting his other foot alongside of its mate.

"Call it a tire puncture, if you like," replied Billy, instinctively feeling around for his shoes, "but for truth, believe me, some Johnny's got a gun and wants to show that it'll shoot."

One thing sure, it did not take the aerial couple very long to precipitate a personal investigation of the matter.

When the young scouts, on active legs, had cleared the entrance of their sleeping quarters, their hearing was assailed by the high and strident tones of a strenuously protesting masculine voice, condemning someone as a "robber," and with added threat of putting the alleged offender "into stripes."

Pushing through the outer rim of a gaping circle of suddenly aroused passengers, mostly pajama-clad, and getting a view of the center of attraction, between the shoulders of the several in uniform—the ship's officers—immediately surrounding the owner of the lashing tongue, the boys saw that the indignant protestant, pallor-stricken and trembling with wrath, was none other than the "constant reader" and claimant of Swiss residence.

And closely facing the man called "Simmons," stood the supposed "prosperity agent," in an entirely new rôle, that of a stern and determined aggressor, holding, with an iron grip, the wrist of the excited declaimer, and, also, pressing under foot a revolver of real killing size, which had evidently dropped to the floor during previous struggle.

"You're at the end of your rope," the dapper individual, turned fighter, was saying, as Billy and

Henri squeezed places in the front rank of the round-up, and this forcefully directed at the fiercely glaring recipient of the positive advice.

"Take your hand off me," menacingly warned the man at bay, "you thief of the night, or I'll break every bone in your body before we're through."

"Much you could do," was the contemptuous reply of the personage behind the pulse-deadening grip. "You could not, to save your soul, do anything straight—look, walk or run; let alone putting up a fair fight."

"What's the cause of this muss?"

The peremptory demand for information from one of the ship's officers.

"That man has stolen a valuable book from me. I caught him in the act."

With the vehement accusation, "Simmons" indulged in another desperate effort to break the vise-like hold maintained by the determined person he was denouncing.

The attempt to free himself from the grip of the detaining hand proving of no avail, the struggling captive appealed to the uniformed viewers of the strenuous performance to interfere in his behalf.

"I have the right to be protected," he cried. "I demand that this man be put under arrest and my property restored to me."

"Which of you, I want to know, fired that 'gun'?"

The insistent and inquisitive official pointed to the weapon under the foot of "DeVries."

Before the query could be answered, if any reply was forthcoming, the captain of the ship, suddenly aroused from the enjoyment of a brief period of much-needed rest by hasty summons, appeared on the scene.

For some reason or other, the representative of supreme power, when he had appraised the situation with a quick eye, displayed no sympathy for the claimant of a great wrong inflicted.

Turning to his subordinates in command, the chief said, fixing an index finger as a directly guiding mark at the now sullen "Simmons":

"Take charge of that man and bring him along."

With the order, "DeVries" immediately relinquished his hold and stepped aside to give place to the authorized custodians, first, however, picking up the revolver from the floor, for safe bestowal in his pocket.

He was then about to follow the officers and

their charge on the way to the captain's room when he noticed the wide-eyed presence of Our Young Aeroplane Scouts in the watching assembly roundabout. Much to the surprise of the boys, the mysterious voyager favored them with a backward turn of the head, an unmistakable invitation to separate from the rest of the curious company and accompany him.

The flying twins were not in the least reluctant when it came to accepting an opportunity of getting on the inside of the affair which had become of acute interest to them.

"Reserved seats for us, I guess," whispered Billy to his pal, as they moved in ready response to the bidding so strangely tendered. "But, believe me, I can't quite catch onto the sudden fancy of the usher for our firm."

The "usher" offered no explanation of the unexpected courtesy as he linked arms with the lads, one on each side, and proceded with them to the place where enlightenment was in prospect.

"Simmons" had ceased to be obstreperous when arraigned before the captain. If the look, however, he turned upon his late captor, as the latter appeared with the young scouts, could have killed, then, surely, "DeVries" would have been instantly stricken in his tracks.

The "Paris and London" personage, though, was apparently not at all disturbed by black looks. Indeed, he was as "cool as a cucumber," and again airing his professional smile with former effectiveness.

In this last display of teeth, it may be stated, he was distinctly the only one of his class. Certainly the captain was not of the mood to "look pleasant," showing in every line of his countenance that he had a "combing" in waiting for somebody or something or other.

"Got that book?"

This sharply accented query was fired at "DeVries."

The individual addressed produced a volume from the interior folds of his coat, and passed it to the official questioner, indicating, as he did so, the hardly perceived crease at the top of the initial binding.

With the keen blade of a "paper knife," from the desk at which the captain was sitting, a slitting process revealed a "pocket," and from which the investigator produced about a dozen sheets of tissue, each covered with letters and figures of a code.

This exhibit served to bring "DeVries" once more to the front, dropping again his impersonation of the genial traveler and with the wire-edge of his manner of address.

"This fellow," he explained to the captain, "expected to furnish spies now operating in America with a new code, the old ones impaired, we have learned, by the ability of the United States intelligence officers to read the existing forms of communication. He has no more right to the name and credentials of Albert Arthur Simmons than myself. The real Simmons, I'll wager my life, was laid low by a dent in the head or knife in the back shortly before this ship cleared harbor. That will be developed later."

Billy nudged his pal. "The blow-up man," was the boy's under-breath assertion, "didn't make the riffle, so this was the last moment thing they tried to put across. Some deep file, that 'DeVries,' to pick up the thread. Who'd a-thought, to look at him, that he was such a tiger of a trailer?"

When the curtain of night had lifted, and the spy convicted, our boys were early on deck to view, in the dim distance, that hazy shore line, which meant

U. S. A., ahead. All else was now of fading importance in the minds of these youthful patriots—with hearts beating high and cheers crowding to their lips.

It was not until the time arrived to pass the barriers on shore that they were again reminded of the existence of the fellow voyager who had sprung the trap on the "bookman," and who had so singularly taken the lads under his wing, so to speak, when about to administer the finishing stroke of his mission.

The hands of the so-called "DeVries" were divided between the shoulders of the flying twins at the moment of departure from the ship, and the accompanying utterance lifted the veil of conjecture as to his oddly bestowed confidence.

"With the regards of Monsieur Ardelle!"

"We might have known that the big chief was behind it all," commented the Bangor boy as he and his pal walked down the gangway into the place that spelled *Home*.

CHAPTER VI

SOME FANCY FLYING

WITHIN twenty-four hours Billy Barry on American soil was an established millionaire and of large account, not only to income tax collectors but as a citizen disposed to devote bank roll, mind and body—all to the service of his country in the hour of stress.

The war was not "far away" to him. He had been right in it for many a day, and well he knew that it was up to the U. S. A. to do the big repeating act in the cause of liberty—and do it now!

With due respect to the heroes, foot, horse and artillery, mighty factors in carrying Old Glory "over the top," the Bangor boy was yet more keenly alive to the ever-growing importance in the titanic struggle of the fighting contingent to which he belonged—the air cavalry!

"If we can't get *through* the 'Hindenburg line' this spring," the young and newly created capitalist remarked to his pal as they took train for the factory town where Barry aeroplanes were in the making; "we can go *over* it this summer!"

What a rush of memories when the young scouts set foot once more in the precincts of the great and now wonderfully expanded industry which had been their training school in the marvelous art of aviation, creative and executive.

In a broad field to the left of the station Billy Barry had first experienced the sensation of flying, where Henri Trouville, too, had made his initial flight.

"I'd give a pretty penny," exclaimed the Maine lad, "if our Capt. Johnson and one Josh Freeman could have this look in on their old stamping grounds!"

"Wouldn't they tread high, though?"

Henri, also, had in mind the veteran airmen in far-off Dover, oft thinking, perhaps, of this very experience of home-coming.

The one o'clock whistle was in full blast when the boys sought entrance at the factory gates, for the first time realizing that unquestioned ingress was no longer the rule and, also, more potently, that there had been some change in themselves, outwardly, at least, in nearly four years absence—years of adventuring in many climes—when the aged watchman, who had long ago been their chief prophet, now "held them up" for investigation.

"Don't you know us, Uncle Bill?" was Billy's reproachful query.

While "Uncle Bill" was adjusting his spectacles Henri advanced the process of recognition with the eager announcement: "Here comes Joe!"

With the lift of the boy's voice, the old man seemed to have been suddenly shaken out of uncertainly as to the identity of the visitors, and with a "whoop" that certainly demonstrated that lung weakness was not among the penalties of his weight of years, the patriarch literally fell upon the necks of the youths, which enfoldment was only broken by the laughing command of the factory "boss," who wanted his turn at warmly greeting the long-absent brother, with a cordial welcome thrown in for the flying twin.

"Just in time to go to work," jovially declared the elder Barry, "and we sure do need first-class 'hands' just now."

"Things going some?" interrogated the junior brother.

"Shoving 'em across double-quick," was the reply.

"Jolly good," rejoiced Billy, "and, Joe," continued the young enthusiast, "put every cent of the pile into the business. It's the way to knock the Kaiser out."

"We'll sit on the lid together, then, youngster," promptly assented the head of the plant. "You and Henri take the jobbing of getting the 'word' for a starter and I'll muss around here as usual."

"But, Joe," explained Billy, "there's the rub. Pard and I are not yet through 'over there,' and we've just got to go back when we've given our little push on this side. Put my share of the money into aeroplane building here, while Buddy and yours truly are doing our level best to somewhat reduce the supply turned out by the Huns."

Joe was obviously disappointed at this pronouncement, for he was counting on the expert assistance of the well-qualified pair, and, further, it was no light matter, considering sentiment, to anticipate another separation from his only brother, when, figuring all hazards, no safe prediction could be made that they would meet again in the flesh.

Like the Barry breed, however, this "piece of

the same kind" was game, and whatever way his thoughts were pulling, not a word of protest passed his lips.

"So be it, laddie," he quietly remarked; "we'll hit 'em both ways, going and coming."

The boys had another touch of "old times" that gave them infinite pleasure when they got into over-alls and in among the factory forces, heartily hailed by many with whom they used to work and winning the approbation of later comers by practical knowledge displayed relative to the varied branches of the industry.

It meant a whole lot to know it all, for amazing figures can be given as to the number of parts and amount of material entering into the construction of an aeroplane. Exclusive of the engine there are hundreds of parts in the structure of a flying machine, and even when built-up sections of the frame are regarded as single parts, there remain nearly two hundred separate pieces to be assembled into a completed product. That is counting out screws, nails and similar items.

As Billy Barry or his pal could tell you, these are the things necessary to build an aeroplane without its engine:

Nails, 4,326; screws, 3,377; steel strappings, 921; forgings, 798; turnbuckles, 276; veneer, 37 square feet; wire, 3,262 feet; varnish, 11 gallons; dope (for dressing wings), 59 gallons; aluminum, 65 pounds; rubber, 34 feet; linen, 20 square feet; spruce, 244 feet; pine, 58 feet; ash, 31 feet; hickory, 1½ feet.

"Busy business, this," said the Bangor lad to his aerial mate during the tour of inspection.

"Makes my fingers itch to get a whack at the old job," was Henri's comment as he viewed the woodworking process, at which he had been a specialist.

"You must remember," jested Joe, "that you fellows are demonstrators by graduation and no longer belong 'downstairs.'"

"I'll admit," said Billy, "that the ground has not been our chief abiding place for some time, but, all the same, it's good to know just what's under you when you're on top of 15,000 feet of ether."

The Barry brothers devoted about half the night to financial discussion, and in the morning Henri was advised by his pal that, having put his late uncle's dollars to work, "we might as well be moving."

It may well be imagined that the Bangor boy

had not yet reached a point where he could easily separate from the war world habit of almost every day running neck and neck with do or die propositions.

The call of dangerous diversion, indeed, was equally forceful in the hearing of both of the youths, and, topped by patriotic fervor, wholly irresistible.

Upon one thing, however, in point of "over here" service, Joe was strenuously insistent—that the young scouts should exhibit down at Washington a pair of the Barry planes, as samples of the U. S. A. contribution to the Allied air cavalry in the war-winning project.

"The Italians have shown their mighty models," lectured the "big brother," "the British machines are there now with the best operators who have been 'through the mill,' and it seems to me that you fellows, with all the 'curves' under your hats, ought to be able to give something of a lift to 'the made in America' brand. How about it?"

"Our hands are up," laughed Billy, "so don't shoot. On to the capital! Liberty motors forever!"

"Hear! Hear!" cried Henri.

"These plans are sure beauties, all right,"

was a later remark by the Bangor boy, when the flying machines they were expected to "put through the paces" had passed their inspection preparatory to shipment, "and we'll get the best out of them that we can," the speaker assured his brother.

"Know you will," confidently asserted Joe, "and, believe me, you youngsters will find that top-notch aviators are 'some punkins' these days in the U. S. A. when you strike the center city on the Potomac."

Billy discovered no reason to subsequently complain that the expert exponents of aviation in this country were not in the van, and, as he put it in his own way, "the flying game is looking up; and the people, I notice, are doing the same thing whenever they hear the buzz."

The motto, "Fly in France," was also "good for sore eyes," he declared, and as well he favored other slogans like, "Fly for Liberty" and "Blindfold the Enemy."

"Here's a man who says there would not be much left of the war if the United States could send a fleet of 500 night bombing aeroplanes into one attack over the enemy lines."

The Bangor boy was regaling his comrade by

reading live extracts from a newspaper, while train-bound for Washington.

"It would help some," commented the reader. "Five or six hundred tons of high explosives planted in a lump would sure clear some ground!"

"Adding some thousands of observing machines, combat machines and pursuit planes," suggested Henri, "ought to complete the 'blindfolding' job."

The young scouts on the rest of the journey had their day dreams of atmosphere filled with the throbbing of motors, and the thunder of air bombs exploding about the ears of Hindenburg and Ludendorff.

It was a gorgeous day when the flying twins set foot in the nation's capital, and, curiously enough, in their first uplook at the sun-filled heavens they saw the darting movements of an aeroplane, which they later learned contained no less distinguished operator than Lieut. Col. Charles Lee, Royal Flying Corps, head of the British aviation mission in the United States, whose aerial performances had been causing thousands of spectators to gasp and turn their eyes away.

"Fast company we've gotten into," observed Billy, as himself and partner were "brushing up a bit" in advance of their visit to the War Department.

The boys were not long in ascertaining that they had something of a "standing" themselves in the paramount profession of the hour—that recognition instantly accorded to men who "do things," and which reputation had preceded them by both foreign and local advices.

Our Young Aeroplane Scouts were indeed welcome to decorate the upper reaches over the Potomac plain with all the evolutions known in aerial warfare, and of such incidents in their meteoric careers as they could be induced to tell about, ready listeners were plenty in official circles.

In the period of a week the lads duplicated aloft all the feats theretofore performed by foremost aviators, and introduced some novelties of their own invention.

Stunts such as the Immelmann turn, the falling leaf, loop the loop and other demonstrations of eminently efficient manipulation were of daily showing by Billy and Henri. They could indorse by varied and long experience the statements by Col. Lee that the performance of these stunts and knowing how to do them had saved the lives of hundreds of

Allied airmen, while inability to perform the evolutions instantaneously had resulted in scores of fatalities which would have been avoided had the aviators been completely familiar with the possibilities of their machines and able quickly to make turns and loops to evade Boche flyers.

What observers on the ground might construe to be the height of foolhardiness are really nothing of the kind—these tricks of the air are absolutely necessary if the fighting aviator is to be able to wriggle out of tight places.

This of passing record in the sojourn of Billy Barry and Henri Trouville on U. S. A. soil, which they could have more quietly and safely served in the rôle of aviation instructors in and out of any of the twenty-four home training stations, but pledged and eager to continue abroad as effective cogs in the intricate and important machinery of the Allied air service.

More than ordinarily grateful for the opportunity of renewing allegiance to the "land of the free" within its gates, more than ever in touch with the golden hope of having years left to run their course in their beloved domain—yet now inspired to offer their all to the wage of war where the brunt of battle must be borne.

The departing day was fixed, and with the flying twins were to travel a hundred or two of their kind, with up-to-date equipment—the vanguard of another U. S. A. invasion of benefit, to be continuous until the Huns should cry, "Hold; enough!"

CHAPTER VII

THE AERIAL TWINS TO THE FRONT

BILLY and Henri were viewing land again for the first time since their farewell to the U. S. A. and Joe Barry—about twelve days from the time of getting under way. With others of the convoyed passenger list, the boys had discarded life preservers, and were preparing to get their trunks ready to leave the ship. No one even dreamed now of a submarine. Indeed, the Bangor boy had just been remarking to his pal that "the 'tin fish' seem to be as wary of you as when we crossed in the other direction."

There had been, throughout the voyage, every concession of precaution to the belief of "dangerous waters," not the slightest speck of light allowed on the vessels in company, in their night plowing of the waves, the ever-present life preserver continuously convenient, and everybody thoroughly posted as to the lifeboat stations—and never a scare-mark in eleven days out.

But now, at the near finish of the voyage, the last day and the last morning, to be exact, 8: 30 a. m., the whistle of the ship on which our lads were passengers began to blow—and right here it may be stated that when a ship's whistle begins to blow in these times after it is on the way to Europe, those experienced will tell you, it is a cue to grab your life preserver and, without a moment's delay, get to your lifeboat station.

If the young scouts proceeded, in response to the emergency signal, a little more leisurely than the average voyager, it was due, no doubt, to the fact of their many previous encounters with the U-boats, regarding which, however, they entertained no careless ideas.

The quick vision of the flying twins had discerned three periscopes in the brief interval between the sound of the whistle and that of the guns from the ship—and then long, steam-like streaks passing the stern of the vessel.

Just about that time, too, the destroyers, which had come out to guide the transports protectively through this part of the danger zone, began to get in their work—and not a gun on any of the transports or destroyers was cold for fully two hours.

"Some hot stuff, this!" exclaimed Billy as he and his pal made a break for the side of the ship where most of the action could be seen. All of the incoming vessels took their own separate courses. They zig-zagged and the sailors wig-wagged. Shot after shot was fired, and the proximity of the guns left a thundering sound in the ears of the onlookers.

"In it again, old top," sang out Henri, gripping the rail, and excitedly watching the destroyers going this way and that, firing into the water at second intervals. They dropped innumerable deadly depth charges into the foaming green—working like a score of cats after a mouse. Oil began to show on the sea surface.

The boys knew what that meant—it meant that where the oil showed one of the Kaiser's nautical murderers had submerged for the last time!

Now a buzzing sound overhead—to the young scouts a mighty familiar whirr—and their eyes instantly directed aloft—two French seaplanes coming to the rescue—dropping bombs from a height of not more than two hundred yards, following with even lower range in the casting of explosives.

"Hit 'em again!"

The Bangor boy was at high key when he contributed this urging to the aerial fellow craftsman, an enthusiastic voicing, though it fell far short of the hearing mark at which it was aimed.

"I wish I had my glass"—this from the Trouville side of the firm, regretting that for the once his precious binocle was not swinging from his shoulder. "I'd give a lot to know if any of 'our crowd' are riding those wings over there."

"Soon for the knowing, Buddy," advised the Barry lad, "for we'll be hitting the port they came from before long."

Though it later developed that none of the aerial bombsters were men whom the boys could call by names at first sight, they found common cause, even outside of professional fraternity, to be immediately chumming with members of the seaplane aiding party, for they all were stoutly attached to LeFane, the king-pin from Rouen.

There was another story waiting for the lads at port—the official announcement that three German submarines had been destroyed and their crews had also gone to Davy Jones' locker, where they would no longer terrorize or murder.

"They sure monkeyed with a buzz-saw this time," was Billy Barry's comment.

About two days after landing Our Young Aeroplane Scouts had augmented realization that they were once more in the "midst of things," so to speak—they arrived on fighting ground while American and German artillery were engaged in a terrific duel. It was 7 o'clock in the evening when the horizon in the vicinity of the U. S. A. front suddenly broke out in a saw-toothed ribbon of flame, created by the pounding of Boche guns. A few minutes later the American guns took a turn at setting the sky ablaze, venting their fury against the enemy batteries. During this roaring din, Billy and Henri reported for duty at aviation headquarters.

"We're here to hook up with Uncle Sam for the straight run through. Our vacation is over, our commissions are O. K., and all we want is the rapid assignment."

This was the form of address of the Maine youth to the commandant, who, it happened, had met the young aviators on the occasion of their previous presentation to General Pershing, and, also, having knowledge of some of the flying exploits standing to the credit of the pair now appealing for further opportunity to distinguish themselves in the upper reaches.

"You young men seem to be giving a hard knock to the figuring fellows who have calculated that the life of the average aeroplane pilot at the front is thirty-one days."

The aviation officer had been told of the extended career of the young scouts in the flying game.

"Maybe you are not counted in the 'average' class," he smilingly added.

"Maybe not," admitted Billy, "if that means over-time luck. But, there's another way, sir," continued the boy, "that pard and I have given the mortality sharps a jolt. Of that I'm sure. They say that it takes an average of 7,000 shells to bring down an aeroplane. I know they're wrong there, for they'd have died of exhaustion trying to count the shots the German Archies fired at us when we carried that message to General Byng!"

Henri grinned his appreciation of his pal's jest. "More truth than poetry in that, after all," was his speaking observation.

"I guess I'm as garrulous as a jaybird to-night," concluded the Bangor boy, turning his attention to the sprays and clusters of vari-colored rockets and star shells shooting up from the enemy trenches, in a manner that indicated excitement in that direction.

These signals and revealing lights hovered above No Man's Land, casting a weird glare over the tangles of weeds and wire and the horizon winced and writhed giant caterpillars of fire as the Sammies loaded and fired their big guns from camouflaged concealments scattered along the countryside.

"Who says the U. S. A. isn't having a hearing in this shake-up now?"

Billy was not seeking an answer from his companion—the reply was giving the earth a quiver every other minute.

The flying twins were not long in finding a place to "hang their bonnets de police," as the Maine youth put it—which happened to be those little drab contraptions made to wear on the side of the head.

Our boys walked in on six other Sammy aviators off duty and occupants of a "Swiss hut" behind the hangars, a shanty put up in sections, which has a sloping roof, was made of quarter-inch pine boards, straight sides, nut clapboards, and some patent tar paper overhead.

One of the "resident" airmen informed Billy that the ventilation was good, light filtered in, and, he added, "also everything else that wants to." As to the round stove, about twelve inches in diameter, located in the center of the room, the informant further advised that it "ate up wood like a sponge sops water." There were four cots on each side of the "remarkable" heater. The flyer who officiated as speaking host explained that "eight of us lived here, but Couzens and Bradford, poor fellows, guessed wrong the other day and paid the price. So their places are yours."

The big guns were still booming when Billy and Henri took a stretch on the vacant bunks and slept as peacefully as they did in the Washington hotel several weeks previously.

They little dreamed, if they dreamed at all, that in the coming day there would be a renewal of their aerial activities in such heroic mold and of such thrilling character as really did happen, and by which they repeatedly challenged the "average figuring" on an aviator's life.

A cold, cheerless rain drizzle at 4:30 in the morning, a vigorous shaking by an orderly to aid the reluctant awakening of a snugly snoozing airman—

that was the dismal scenery, the unearthly hour and the drag-out to which Billy opened his eyes.

He heard a voice saying:

"Barry—5 o'clock patrol."

A bit out of training, and lately cultivated taste for an extra forty winks at dawn-time had Billy inclined to delay rising for five or ten minutes, necessitating another hand disturbance by the rousing authority, which started the rolling out process, the hasty gulping down of a cup of fast cooling black coffee brought by the summoning individual, a scramble into clothes and a start for the hangars on a dead run.

Three others, the boy noticed, had the same assignment, but Henri was not in the list, and still sleepily unconscious of the fact.

The quartette made their getaway in semi-darkness, spiraled high and hit out for the lines in patrol formation, taking another lift when once in reach of the Teuton Archies, Billy's machine following the other three. By this time the planes were headed straight toward the rising sun, and in the edge of the yellow glare the Bangor boy had sudden sight of a pair of Boches flying a short distance inside their own lines.

It was not customary to break out of patrol formation, but this Barry lad had been routed out of the "wrong side of the bed," and, too, he had not been in an air scrap for quite awhile, which made him somewhat forgetful of technical requirements!

So he pulled out of the course his companions were flying without attempting to attract their attention and started across the trails of the German machines, desiring to get between them and the sun. By their elongated tail fins he recognized them as Rumplers—two-seated fighting planes.

Billy got well behind and above them without being seen. Then he piqued downward on the rear flying enemy machine and opened fire, spraying bullets across the plane and back, the way a whitewing sprays the street, making sure to get it all wet.

Nothing much happened that the daring young aviator could see—the Rumpler just pitched forward in a nose dive and went down the whole half mile to the ground.

The Bangor boy had come down so low that the second Rumpler was above him. The Hun started to attack the American pilot, just as the latter had the other German above.

"Tack-tack-tack-tack," sputtered the Teuton gun,

and Billy saw thin gray trails go streaking past him. That gray smoke meant incendiary bullets. At night they would have glowed. They were compounded of phosphorus and were meant to explode the adversary's petrol and burn him up.

The Maine youth's machine was nimble and turned around so quickly that when the boy banked around again he was behind the Kaiser outfit.

Our flyer got in only a few shots that time, for his opponent did the turning trick himself, succeeding to rear position—the machines circling like two fish chasing each other around an aquarium.

By partly looping the loop and twisting right side up at the upper part of the circle Billy came above the German flyer and got a fine bead on him.

"Spat, spat, spat," went the Barry gun.

The Boche observer stood up in his place, leaned over the side and slipped out his safety strap downward, turning over and over as he dropped. Then there was a flash and the whole machine seemed to burst into flames and fall to pieces at the same time, as if a shell had blown it apart. It was the fuel tank exploding. One of Billy's incendiary bullets had hit the mark. What became of the pilot of the stricken Rumpler the young aviator did not see. The moment he was in the sky alone the Archies began shelling as hard as they could to get revenge for their lost airmen.

As the Bangor boy turned in the direction of the friendly lines, he noted an invasion of a section of No Man's Land by German infantry, moving into battered earthworks that once formed the French firing line. Other masses were moving up in support, and already the nearest shell holes were heaving and boiling over with the restless heads and shoulders of men about to renew the advance. The French battalion opposing the attack had gone to earth in little isolated groups, grimly determined to hang on to the end.

The fire from the Germans increased until the air was alive with their bullets. It was the concentrated fire which always precedes the rush to close quarters. The blue-gray figures were beginning to appear full length above the shell holes, their loose, flapping uniforms and hideous gas masks giving them the appearance of demons.

Suddenly into the smoke and murk of battle there dived an American aeroplane!

Fifty feet from the ground it flattened out and skidded along the line, dropping its bombs among the bewildered Germans. Wheeling swiftly at the flank of the attack, it came skimming back like a swallow charging a swarm of flies, its machine guns enfilading the advancing foe and driving them back to their burrows.

A storm of German bullets swept through the planes, and a black flame-centered burst of shrapnel smothered the aeroplane in vapor. The watching infantry saw splinters fall from its quivering frame and the silvery fabric of the under wings was torn in several places by shell splinters.

But the daring pilot finished his course and ascended into the smoke clouds, leaving the panic-stricken enemy clinging to his shell holes, too shaken and thinned to press the attack further.

The hero of this danger-defying feat in his getaway passed within a hundred feet of a high-flying patrolman named Barry, just registering a triumph of his own.

It was Henri Trouville who had held the German attack!

CHAPTER VIII

HUMAN HURRICANE IN ACTION

BILLY knew by the markings of the passing plane that it had been a Sammy boy who engineered the thrilling and effective drive he had just witnessed, but he failed to identify the gallant performer sitting low in the cockpit, so swift the departing flight of the hero, and the latter too busy a minute or two later in nursing a development of failing strength in his damaged machine for the sparing of a backward glance at the high-circling comrade by whom he had dashed.

The Bangor boy, assured by observation and short-trailing venture that the plucky aviator was pretty sure of getting back to his aerodrome without a tumble, again turned his attention to the fighting ground below.

Little by little the German supports were coming up, advancing by short rushes over the open, reinforcing their comrades by twos and threes, in spite of the opposing fire. Scores and scores of their dead littered No Man's Land, but gradually the strength of the attacking line was made good, and the shell holes again began to heave and boil as men rose from the lower cover and laid hold of the rims to assist them over the top.

Then suddenly they were over and away, little spurts of humanity belched out of the crated field, gathering into a seething blue-gray rushing mass, hopelessly outweighing the handful of defenders. But before the mass could gain full momentum, a familiar snoring hum sounded above the din of battle, and out of the low-lying haze swept a covering aeroplane, another "guardian angel," and again an American!

Billy, with intent interest, had greatly reduced the altitude at which his mechanical "wasp" had been buzzing, and could easily spot the colors of this new candidate for "clean up" honors.

The bombs of the charging aviator dropped among the advancing Germans, dispersing those who escaped the flying fragments, and his machine guns swept them out of sight into the shell holes.

Up again and down again, often rocking madly in the air gusts from a barrage salvo, just as often performing wilder maneuvers to confuse the gunners and riflemen who se rched for him incessantly, the "human hurricane" encouraged the resisting infantry on his side and scattered death and confusion among their foes.

A German battle plane dashed out to drive him away.

And here was where Billy Barry "mixed in."

Like a streak of light he sent his staunch little craft in a nose dive at the Hun flyer, came down on the latter's tail and sent him cart-wheeling behind his own lines.

Then the rattle of the gun with the Bangor boy behind it sent more Germans to cover, and he was scooting on the now lifting trail of the fiery catapult which had cut such a wide swath in the enemy ranks.

This was the finish of the conflict, with the Germans securely checked.

Billy was soon flying closely parallel with the comrade who had created the last "stir," and both headed for their own lines.

It was not until they landed that the Maine youth discovered that the "rusher" in his company was none other than "Pure Grit" Patterson, the chap who had officiated as spokesman when our flying twins joined the "big six" colony in the Swiss hut.

"Saw you butt into the game," genially remarked the aviator with the rightly applied title, "and you sure sent the would-be tackler of yours truly on the quick backtrack. Much obliged, old boy."

"Say, brother, you're a cool 'un," admiringly exclaimed Billy, "and I'm handing it to you for a plunger!"

The straightforward compliment elicited a broad smile from its recipient, and a neat parry by the remark: "I see you've been hunting trouble somewhere yourself"—pointing to a lot of bullet holes in the wings and fuselage of the Bangor boy's machine.

"Nicked up a little bit," acknowledged Billy, "but your outfit will need more repairs than mine."

He didn't know that a worse wrecked aeroplane than either of the two mentioned, over which mechanicians were "fussing" as Patterson and himself passed on the way to the shanty, had carried his very own pal through a powder and lead storm a little while before.

That same "pal" had a bandaged hand, but a cheery voice when he greeted the incomers from a folding chair behind the eccentric stove.

"What've you been up to?"

This quick query from young Barry when he caught sight of the linen-wrapped "fin" of his chum.

"Started to hunt you and the machine ran away with me," jocularly replied Henri. Then, more seriously, he added: "Saw a chance to 'hit the line' and went through. A 'bunch' of our fellows were in close quarters and I had a load of bombs that needed exploding. Got rid of the 'freight' and here I am."

"So you were the lad that 'came across' in advance of 'Pure Grit' here. Well, I'll send for two medals in the morning."

Just then the commandant strode into the hut, and in time to hear the Bangor boy's remark.

"Make it three, young man, while you're at it, for I've just heard from a balloon observer that he 'glassed' a fellow about your size putting down two big machines that had no business getting in your way. The French give crosses for this kind of thing, and when the first badges of honor that shall be made in America come over, the roll will be called for a trio at which I'm now looking."

When the addressing officer had departed, Bob Rawlins, a crackerjack air fighter himself, gravely proceeded to decorate with chalked crosses a square of tar paper at the end of the shanty, which the inmates used as a blackboard, and further demonstrated his ability as a "rough draft" artist by these words, in scroll effect: "This is our busy day—please be brief."

In their few hours of leisure these daredevils of the air are ever addicted to "'smileage" entertainment.

But, alas! brave and merry Bob Rawlins went out the next day and never came back.

Being off duty for a brief period, Henri, by reason of his burned fingers, and Billy, by the temporary lack of a flying machine, undergoing fixing process, the boys got a ride in a snorting little side car and a visit to the American trenches—just what trenches are everywhere—except that some are muddier than others—but they had Sammies in them, and that alone was worth while to the young scouts.

Spattering through a slightly damaged village, with only a few villagers left in it, they, in the way of incidents, saw an American soldier carrying a tiny girl across the street—an extraordinary muddy, gummy and pathetic little waif; they observed another Sammy boy reasoning with a mule, with earnest listeners about; American soldiers "toting" water, diving into the ruins of shell-smashed houses for bits of wood to build cooking fires when darkness came, and standing guard and doing errands.

Where now the city-pale civilians? The fellows, too, who had begun to run to fat and bent shoulders? The same, and yet not the same, these fighting factors "over there," brown, hard and thick!

The portion of the American lines that our boys visited lay low through a swampy country, cut here and there by sluggish streams—the German trenches, higher up, from seventy-five to three hundred yards distant. The day was foggy, misty and damp, a day neither side works, but the gunners stand by like cats watching a mousehole. If the sun comes out for a moment they begin to register. Between times they sit in their dugouts waiting for a call. On the German side they play "skat." The Americans favor "rum."

By the passing of a night in bivouac, however, the young scouts had the opportunity of seeing that sodden field in the brighter day ensuing, enlivened by a glorious moving picture of American troops going "over the top"—side by side with French soldiers making a tremendous drive against the Germans in a destructive raid, capturing all objectives in their 600-yard advance.

But there must be heeding of their own call— the call of the aerodrome and hangars, and so the splashing return of the young aviators to the point from which they started.

In friendly argument with the infantry officer, to whom the boys owed the favor of the trip, Billy smilingly asserted:

"It's about six hundred miles, sir, from this front to Berlin. It might take you people on foot years to make the trip, but our flyers in the air can do it in four hours! Keep your eye on the Yanks, Major, when they thicken the topside!"

"More power to them," cried the major; "any way to get there. But," he chuckled, "we did that six hundred yards very nicely this morning, eh?"

"You bet that was a dandy performance," heartily conceded the young aviator, "and just the kind of stuff to whoop up things in the U. S. A."

"Now, pal," said Billy that night, "until you get that rag off your fist your job will be to take care of the stove. The performance by which you got the singeing is well worth a week to think about, and if you didn't already have the *Croix de Guerre* it would be hung on you before Sunday comes. Lie quiet, old top, until your grip is good again."

"Not me," protested Henri. "I'll be wearing a glove to-morrow, and if any assignment goes up on that blackboard for you, it goes for me, too."

"Hardhead," scolded the Bangor boy, as he kicked out of his shoes preparatory to a tumble into his bunk.

A softened mood was his, though, before his eyes closed in sleep—for "Pure Grit" came in with the sad news of "Bob's error of judgment."

It so happened that the aviators of "Swiss hut" residence had nary a "call" the next morning, for the fog was "thick enough to be cut with a knife," as Billy remarked after early lookout, and coming back to fire a remark at his pal—"now you'll have to be good."

With an extra amount of rest forced upon them, and the indulgence of an extended sleep period in the morning, the young scouts, as the day grew older, developed a restless streak, and fairly jumped at a second invitation of their recently acquired friend, Major Coombs, to journey forward to the American trenches, where the weather was not then preventing active operations.

"It will have to be an after-dark exhibit entirely this time, for it's a mighty late start and some sloppy sledding ahead for the old car," observed the major, "but I don't think you fellows will mind that after all the siesta you've had to-day."

Billy and Henri certainly did not "mind" any excursion just then with a "something doing" attachment.

It chanced that the curtain of fog lifted in the early evening, with war throbs a plenty in staging behind it. The trench scene at night is, indeed, thrilling and inspiring. On the firing platforms the men stand near their rifles. Others splash through the trench, sometimes slipping from the buckboards into water above their knees. They are probably going out on patrol. If the position is near the enemy lines hardly a word is ever spoken, and when a word is necessary it is spoken in a whisper. Far away to one side of the position a white stream shoots up to the sky and breaks into white balls that throw a light as if from powerful electric batteries. The reflections show wire entanglements and scrubby bushes on the hills nearby; then the lights die out.

All the while there is the intermittent roar of

guns and a whistle as of express trains as projectiles of different caliber go rushing over the American trenches seeking a German target. The Sammy boys have become so accustomed to such sounds that now they apparently pay no attention to them. Every now and then the sound of a shell explosion is audible, but most of the time the artillery targets at night are too far back for the men to hear the projectiles explode.

Every man in the line at all times has his eyes open for two kinds of colored rockets. One is green and the other is red. The first means asphyxiating gas and the other calls for a barrage. And the green light to the man in the line means more than anything else, for in a gas attack they know that their lives often depend upon the speed in which the gas masks are adjusted after an alarm is given.

Billy Barry and Henri Trouville had had the experience of seeing the green lights break through the black screen and were well aware of the penalty of inattention.

Intermittently during this night of their watching with American troops in the trenches there came from different parts of the line the single crack of a rifle, as a sniper fired, or the rapid spit of a machine gun at some suspected point or object, for the machine gunners shoot first and ask questions afterward.

When the flying twins were speeding on the backtrack in the major's car a clear day had dawned, and a later look aloft revealed to their keen vision another phase of the war game with which they were even more familiar than with trench fighting—observation aeroplanes in the usual group of three, the German practice in such trips, and a trail of smoke from bursting shells following them across the sky.

"A little business in our line," was the Bangor boy's say to his chum, as they hove in sight of the shanty they called "headquarters."

CHAPTER IX

BILLY AS AN ARTFUL DODGER

THE hut was uninhabited when the young scouts entered therein, which prompted Billy to remark that "everybody's working but us." Just then the inevitable orderly stuck his head in the door with a call for "Barry."

"Present," promptly stated the Bangor boy. "What's to do?"

"Plenty," was the reply. "You're wanted at the hangars."

"What's the matter with me?" demanded Henri.

"No order for you."

The Trouville lad settled in the folding chair, the picture of disconsolate resignation. His blistered hand was causing considerable pain, but to him the lesser hurt than this being left behind.

"Never mind, old top," consoled Billy, "you'll be pounding the Boches again in a few days, and perhaps I won't be gone long on this trip, whatever it is."

At the place of aeroplane housing the Maine youth found the others of the existing shanty colony whom he had missed upon arrival a few moments previously. Six machines were lined up before the hangars, and mechanicians were hustling about, tuning them up for flight; motors were ripping the air with short roars; propellers were spinning in spurts, and everything was abustle. One or two of the other pilots were already seated in their machines, "Pure Grit" Patterson on the near side to Billy and making good as a hailer of the latest comer above the general commotion.

But the outcry of welcome was finished on the run, for just then a mechanician took away the blocks under the wheels of the Patterson plane and the "Human Hurricane" was off for the rise, immediately following the flight master, or, as the French say, the *"chef de patrol"*—"Daredevil" Hanford it happened to be—who got away with a great roar and spiraled up, turning always to the right as he climbed.

The rest of the flying company turned to the left in the uplift, making it easy to know which machine carried the leader. Billy was number four in rising against the wind, and he noted that the directing flyer was headed away north of northeast, about the direction in which himself and pal had seen the covey of Hindenburg's aerial Uhlans when the lads were coming back from the trenches.

It was quite evident that the enemy craft had done considerable receding since that viewing, for Pershing's cloud-hurdling "bunch" were traveling quite far afield without as yet encountering anything in the way of high-up opposition.

From below, however, there was directly some evidence that the Sammy aviators were not to escape the usual warm reception tendered overhead invaders of territory beyond their own lines.

Flying to the extreme left of the balance of the trouble-hunting excursionists, Billy was constrained to quit the straight-line method of travel and go to "snaking," in order to keep the Boche range finders and pointers guessing, the regulation practice when shelling begins. The boy was sailing among big, black puffs of smoke that blossomed with dull roars, above, below and on all sides.

On an excursion like this an aviator does not lack for exercise—twisting in his seat, keeping up the lookout for enemy planes and shells. First a look far back over the left shoulder and up—then the right shoulder and up—then to the left and down and a veer to the right for a peek under the lower left plane—then to the right and down and a peek under the lower right plane—then a dip downward for a look over the upper plane, then the whole thing over and over again.

Young Barry, accustomed to this sort of gyration, had not reached the "played out" stage by any means, though the strain of such flight had been extended beyond anticipation and nothing to enliven so far beyond the shell-dodging maneuvers.

But, now, having an eye ahead for a few minutes in endeavor to locate the flight leader, Billy had sudden recall to the attitude of roundabout attention.

A sharp tack-tack-tack-tack had broken out behind him—machine-gun fire. The young scout straightened out and looked back, staring at a Maltese cross on the planes of a Boche two-gun, two-seated fighting machine as fast as the one which he was driving.

That momentary inattention on the part of the Bangor boy put him at a disadvantage. In the quick thought that followed, Billy had reason to fear that the Teuton would get him, if the threatening pilot happened to be a fellow of experience. Already the gray streaks—trails of incendiary bullets—were shooting past the Barry machine on the left—intended to set fire to the patrol tank and send the lad down in flames.

Billy "snaked," watching the smoke trails edge nearer. The Boche began to get a bead with the fixed forward gun timed to shoot through his propeller and aimed by pointing his whole machine. The smoke trails came closer.

The young scout, cool again and cunning as a fox, manipulated his machine as if for climbing, and, instead, swerving downward to the left. The feint worked. The boy was below the Boche, out of reach of both the fixed gun in front and the free one operated by the man in the rear seat of the big German battleplane.

Whatever the conceived next move of the Barry lad, it was never executed, for something just then hit the big machine overhead amidship, so to speak, and the whole fabric went groundward like a tower-top shaken out of balance by an earthquake.

The tremendously intervening "something" was one of those steel-beaked drives engineered by that reckless but most efficient air artist, "Pure Grit" Patterson, who, however, this time got more than he bargained for in the terrific impact that sent the object of attack on the plummet course.

Billy saw that the rescuer was having trouble with the machine just used as a ripping instrument, and also witnessed an exhibition of skill on the part of the operator in working the long slide act toward solid surface far below.

The Bangor boy steered in pursuit of the volplaning comrade—himself seeking land in mighty rapid descent.

When Billy "hit bottom," it was within an area of No Man's Land, which, so far as one could see, was barren, empty, uptorn, yet with certain landmarks still left, such as a shell-tattered stone farmhouse and an old cowstable whose walls were still standing at a feeble height.

Within fifty feet of these latter "remains," our young scout sighted his "catapult friend" calmly sitting in the cockpit of his damaged machine and contemplating the surroundings with the same degree of languid interest as he probably would bestow upon the surface of a training field when first alighting from an easy practice flight. The actual nerve-trying experience of the preceding minutes had left no mark on the demeanor of this unshakable person.

The same old grin was in evidence when Billy leaped from his aeroplane and approached at quick-step, and it was the same old drawl in the greeting words of the stranded aviator:

"Glad to see you, pard. Was just thinking about being a bit lonesome."

Young Barry could not refrain, for the life of him, from laughing at this living picture of unconcern.

Attendant upon mirthful outburst he remarked:

"I guessed it was you on the way down, and now, even if you didn't have your face with you, I could swear to your manner."

"It would be the proper thing now, I think, for me to give an imitation of a young man trying to doctor an ailing aeroplane," observed Patterson, climbing out of his machine, and gravely inspecting the craft from stem to stern.

Billy here proceeded to shine as an expert "fixer," and in a brief period of time found and so reduced the dislocation in the running gear of the badly jarred cruiser that it responded to a test of assurance, which satisfied both aviators of sufficient carrying power to get "Pure Grit" back where he started from.

Before taking to the air again, however, Patterson scrutinized the expanse aloft through the powerful binoculars he carried, desirous, no doubt, of "placing" whatever might be on the wing in the locality, and fixing the status, if possible, of such craft, if any in sight, as to being of the friendly brand, or otherwise.

"We're evidently 'monarchs of all we survey' this blessed minute," remarked "Pure Grit" after his careful viewing of the upper reaches. "There may be a Hun or two camouflaging behind those clouds over there, but no place to hide, as far as I can see, on the way we're going. I'll be switched, though, if I can figure just where our 'bunch' have got to!"

When taking the rise and soaring homeward, the two aviators had cause to believe they had located at least one of the Sammy machines some distance westward, when noting fluffy, white cloudlets of anti-aircraft shrapnel emanating from the Teuton lines—enemy gunners trying to lay the range of the flying invader. But through the glasses both Billy and his accompanying comrade were reasonably convinced that the menaced member of their crowd was making good as a dodger and getting high enough to pull clear of any ground reach.

The rather shaky condition of Patterson's plane, anyway, precluded side trips of investigation, and the Bangor boy proposed to run along with "Pure Grit" until he saw the latter safely landed in front of their own hangars.

Passing the wide, bare strip of yellowish brown, marking No Man's Land between the opposing lines, the returning airmen presently looked down upon the maze of American trenches, intertwining and interlocking, seated a considerable depth in the earth, behind a tiny, hair-like line that marked the advance firing positions. Then little even rows marking the posts supporting the barbed-wire entanglements. All this so shell-pitted that it resembled, from aloft, the footprints of a thousand dogs in the sand on some seaside.

Still further along and the aviation base was in sight, which haven brought the incoming flyers into circling descent, a timely opportunity for Patterson, whose aeroplane had about reached its hold-up limit.

They learned that all of the starting aerial party had now returned save Jimmy Bayles, an Ohioan, which reported absence prompted the Bangor boy to express the wonder if it had not been Jimmy who was aboard the flying target of the shell shooters, which exhibit of high-rising explosives he and "Pure Grit" had noted during the homeward drive.

"If it were Bayles," added Billy, "it looked like he was beating the gunning game in fine style, and he ought to be in by this time."

Now Jimmy Bayles belonged to the "Swiss hut" coterie, which was mourning the loss of one of their number within a comparatively few hours, "Brave Bob," making it doubly trying to entertain the belief that another "bully good fellow" had so soon followed his comrade on the "never come back" trail.

When Barry and Patterson reached the shanty quarters it was nearly noon, and they found Henri rid of the bandage on his injured hand, replaced by a glove, which fact the "impatient patient" was quick to impress upon that partner of his who had insisted on the "stay at home" cure for the Trouville lad.

"The doc says I'm as good as new," proclaimed the unwilling invalid, "and I've been around looking at the only 'loose' machine in camp since mine was busted—it's a two-seater, but"—here a grin at Billy —"I haven't decided yet who I want for company in the next run out."

"It ought to be me," suggested "Pure Grit," "since

I've got a 'sick' aeroplane on my hands, and short a job until it emerges from the 'hospital.' "

"I'll consider applications in the order of filing," laughed Henri, "reserving the right to reject any and all bids."

The smile on the boy's face, however, quickly died away when he heard the first gloomy surmise as to the fate of Jimmy Bayles, to whom he had taken quite a fancy.

"Say, Buddy," he exclaimed, addressing Billy, "you and I have always been lucky in the searching business, and, believe me, I'd like to have a try at locating Jimmy, if he still has a breath in him! If his machine got plugged there's a fighting chance that he might have made the slide into No Man's Land —he was a dandy operator, you know."

Patterson shook his head. " 'Fraid, brother, that if Jimmy went down, it was into German trenches. The only machine of our kind we saw coming in was skylarking directly over the Hun guns."

"Bother to your dark figuring," persisted young Trouville. "Isn't that 'hunch' of yours working to-day, pal?"

This question earnestly put to Billy.

The Bangor boy had to acknowledge that his premonitory power was not acute in this case.

"But I'll tell you what I'll do, old top," he volunteered, "if Commandant Gibbs will give us leeway, there's one by the name of Barry who will sit with you in the machine that goes to hunt Jimmy Bayles."

"Go to it, fellows," cried Patterson, persuaded to lend hope to the proposed venture of Our Young Aeroplane Scouts, "and more power to the expedition!"

An aeroplane doubly manned left the American hangars precisely at 2 p.m.

CHAPTER X

THE SEARCH FOR JIMMY BAYLES

WHEN Billy and Henri flew over the American lines in search of their missing aviator comrade, the first named lad guided the outgoing machine on a straight line and in the direction he had fixed in his memory as a lead to where he had last seen the cleverly managed aeroplane dodging ground fire.

The pilot's purpose was to make this locality a center of flight radiation in all directions over open territory, in which unoccupied area, perchance, the absent flyer had, if crippled, sought landing place. Our boys realized, of course, that they were drawing the "long bow" in nursing any great degree of confidence in the success of their mission.

But, as Henri had declared, just in advance of the expedition, "we've been lucky in the rescue business," there might be a repetition of fortunate outcome in the present venture. Upon "might be," then, all hope was hanging—though, apparently, by a mighty slender thread.

Fourths of July could equal in any fraction the hullabaloo of one night I spent in that devastated region, where there's hardly a square inch of normal ground. Just imagine what it was to me, then a tenderfoot, to be alone in a wilderness of desolation, in blackest darkness, with shells screaming overhead, some dropping within fifty yards of my shivering shape, and all accompanied by a terrific bombardment and cannon roar. My engine stopped during a night flight, and I didn't know or care where I landed, if only I wasn't 'scattered' when I hit. And during that terrible attack I was lost for six hours, twice crossed No Man's Land, and finally getting back to my post through mud, in places, up to my knees—this amid, as I stated before, tumultuous roaring of cannon, explosion of shells, bursting of high explosives and shrapnel, bullets whizzing over ears and head. You fellows know how they kill the nerve in a bad tooth so you can chew most anything. That's what happened to me. It broke me of gun-shyness."

"I noticed," put in Billy, "that you didn't seem much disturbed the other day when about half the German army took a pop at you as you bucked the line in a mile push."

"Pure Grit" presented a hand-palm in gesture of self-defense, and then placed the same hand on Henri's shoulder with the earnest remark:

"Here's the boy you want to exploit, if that's the ticket for the evening. He had less to hold him up than I when he got through."

"Now *it is* time to retire," asserted the Trouville lad, reaching for his blanket roll.

In less than five hours it was time to get up—in a hurry. Something "unpleasant" was happening outside.

The aviators had an emergency call, which made them hustle like metropolitan firemen when the alarm gong sounds, and all on account of a German aeroplane introducing a brand-new sample of Hun methods while flying over the American sector, namely, dropping rubber balls some twenty inches in diameter, filled with liquefied mustard gas, with effect not serious, but the Sammy troops infuriated by what they called "dirty warfare."

Billy was the first of the aerial force to reach the hangars, completing attiring process on the run, and he had a lead of several minutes on the others in getting aloft to engage the marauder.

But lightning climber though he was, the Bangor

boy failed to get a shot at the gas disturber, so rapid the latter's retreat when he observed the aerodrome activities below. The young scout, however, "sprung something" in his machine by the racing effort, and, although he was the first up, was the first down as well.

As luck would have it, the enforced landing was on the right side of a stretch of marsh, and in a well-beaten path here running from angle to angle of the American trenches, the grounded aeroplane rolling within a few yards of a sturdy little stone bridge spanning a thirty-foot-wide creek.

Beyond the bridge was another smashed-up village. The old cemetery at one side had apparently been the scene of a hard fight at some earlier day, for loopholes had been knocked through the stone walls and some of the tombstones had been over-turned by shell fire. In the village itself the sides of the houses exposed to German fire had been torn away and only a few jagged gables thrust up above the prevailing monotony of ragged masonry.

The path in which the young scout alighted, for a defensive point, was considerably exposed, for only occasionally were embankments of sandbags. Billy immediately started the work of overhauling his aeroplane to ascertain just where it was "out of whack," and, while bending over to the task, the ping of a bullet close to his right ear caused the boy to seek full-length position on the ground, the "pancake act" of the experienced campaigner when a sniper catches him unawares. He did not think for a minute that any Sammy in the near vicinity had made him the victim of error, for his identity as an American flyer had been fully established before he got to earth.

Cautiously crawling beneath the wings of the machine, the aviator was a keen looker for the probable location of the sniper, which he finally concluded must be somewhere on a road that had been raised above the level of the bogland, for no one knows how many centuries. Realizing the fact that he would certainly risk perforation at the hands of the hidden sharpshooter if he attempted to further operate as a mechanician in this open space, Billy decided to cross the bridge for an interview with the Yankee lads he knew to be entrenched in that direction. While moving Indian fashion around a bend just ahead, the Bangor boy noted bullet marks on the trees, little pebbles kicked up on the surface of the path and, also, that the wet gray stone of the old bridge had been scarred and chipped—indicating, he figured, that the lurking marksman had before tried his aim hereabouts.

And that he thrice tried it again on Billy the lad could testify before he reached a less exposed position among the ruins across the bridge. There, hearing voices, who should the young scout run into but his friend, the major, and recent host in the car journey to and from the trenches.

This officer and a companion, also of commissioned rank, and an old deer hunter, were discussing the very "sniper" problem which had engaged the Maine youth with practical illustrations a few minutes previously, and an experience that the young flyer made haste to tell about to these interested listeners.

The major had his plans to send the pesky Hun shouting home to Valhalla. Speaking of the bend where Billy heard the bullets sing, he remarked:

"They snipe there all the time. Got one of my men last night."

If this verified the observation belief of the keen-eyed Barry, he did not indulge in any relation of his visual prowess, but took up the more important issue of getting his aerial cruiser where he could "tinker" it into going shape again without chancing better success on the part of the concealed sharpshooter.

This transfer of the non-working machine to a safer "shop" was speedily accomplished by the application of husky man power, and as speedily the expert pilot remedied the trouble which had checked his flight.

All ready to be off again, Billy was taking an up-view to ascertain if any of the other flyers from his camp were still in the air, and with an eye, too, wide open for any "wings" that might be carrying pilots of the opposite brand.

Enemy or friendly, it was not an aeroplane aloft, however, that had anything to do with the Bangor boy's sudden leaving of the ground two or three minutes after starting sky study.

CHAPTER XI

DARING DEED OF RESCUE

THE young scout in scanning the upper reaches caught sight of one of the observation balloons, above the camp at the rear of the American lines, lifting to an unusual height, and over a cloud of shrapnel smoke. With the aid of his field glasses, Billy could see, for sure, that the big gas bag was adrift, and being wind-driven at the rate of some twenty-five miles an hour toward the German front.

Instantly surmising that the balloon cable had been severed by fire from the Teuton high-velocity naval guns, which devote their time to shelling the back areas, the Barry lad was prompted to put his machine through the paces in endeavor to reach the great envelope going astray in time for a pickup of the aeronaut—Billy having noted only one man in the basket—should the latter get down, either by parachute or cord ripping of the upholding fabric, before reaching the all too near enemy positions.

The aeroplane the Bangor boy was driving, in addition to a speeding power of two and a half miles a minute, had also carrying capacity for two, and its pilot was at his best when it came to a venture with chief requirements of quick thinking, daring and consummate skill.

When the major emerged from his dugout in the ruined village, in which he had stopped for a minute out of the wind to light a cigar, he saw a flying machine skimming the level of what had once been a well-kept street, and the dashing air departure of his late aviator visitor.

Billy surely was "going some" when he fairly started on the high line for the far less rapidly moving balloon.

"Queer," thought the boy, "why the man doesn't pull the cord, jump with the 'umbrella,' or something.   He must be shell-shocked."

The young aviator had a memory, from his own brief experience in the observation-balloon service, of seeing in the basket bottom of a hauled-down gas bag the unconscious form of an observer who had suffered "shrapnel shake-up," the victim otherwise unhurt, but taking some time to recover.

In this instance, though, the swift-flying airman

soon discovered that the balloon man had not lost his senses, giving evidence of the fact by his act of throwing overboard, while drawing nearer to the German lines, all his maps and documents.

It was not, however, until within 1,000 yards of the advanced enemy positions that the ripping cord operated to bring the balloon to earth.

By this time Billy and his aeroplane was, so to speak, "right on top" of the descending performance, and so sharp his own downturn that the machine he was guiding touched earth just as the aeronaut leaped from his basket.

The young scout was all voice for a second in shouting to the somewhat bewildered balloon observer to "catch on."

The latter's recovery of wits apparently was instantaneous, for he "caught on" as quick as wink, and the doubly weighted mechanical bird, like a flash, wheeled away for the rise with the immense billowing fabric of the fallen balloon between it and the Boche trenches, a voluminous shield that served well as an aid to ground clearing without the application of enemy explosives.

Billy and his companion were a half-mile further away, and a quarter mile further up before the astonished gunners in the rear kicked up their powder storm, and then without effect as far as the occupants of the Barry machine were concerned.

"Where'd you come from?" queried the balloonist, when he had become more used to the breathing at a speed of 150 miles an hour.

"Maine," replied Pilot Barry.

"I meant a few minutes ago," suggested the questioner, laughing.

"Oh, just cloudland," stated Billy.

Talking being a task, with the insistent motors going full blast, the fast-riding pair gave all attention to the anticipated landing at the balloon station.

"Hello, Gibson," was the ground officer's hail to Billy's aerial fellow traveler, when the aeroplane came to a standstill after a smooth drop, "we were thinking that you had surely gone on a long visit to the Kaiser."

The hand-grip that "Gibson" got from the speaker, however, evidenced more of an earnest welcome than indicated by the seemingly careless form of address.

"I am indebted to this young gentleman from Maine for timely intervention; otherwise, this camp would have been short an observer," stated the balloonist that the Bangor boy had pulled out of Boche clutches, and then proceeded to give the details of the rescue.

Billy was immediately the central figure of a group of members of the "lookout service," who certainly gave the lad lively impression of being an honored guest.

An exclamation—"look there!"—from someone on the outer edge of the circle, and with a pointing gesture upward, suddenly commanded all eyes in turn skyward. A squadron of German aeroplanes —through instantly fixed glasses seven were counted—had broken out of the clouds and were endeavoring to sweep across the American lines—attracting a storm of elevated shots from Sammy guns.

The Bangor boy, who had been wondering what had become of the aviation "crowd" to which he belonged, was now to be assured on this particular point, for hardly were the enemy invaders in passing vision, a matter of two or three minute, when in an opposite direction the blue canopy above was speckled with darting dots concentrating upon the aerial path of the approaching bombplanes operated by the Huns.

Young Barry's "good-bye" to the balloon observers on foot was a snapshot farewell, indeed, and if he passed a word of thanks to the men who gave his machine the hasty push, it was not audible, so quick the starting of the motor.

As Billy afterward said, his shanty comrades "beat him to it," but not altogether depriving the late comer of an opportunity to do his "little bit" in the high-up shindy.

By the time the young scout reached the vicinity of the aerial combat then in progress, six machines to a side, he was rampant to mix in, but diverted from the general melee by the sight of a single Boche cruiser separate from the balance of the whirling wasps and so high against the then cloudless dome that its aluminum body looked like a small flaming cross glinting in the sunlight.

Toward that shining mark Billy climbed like a rocket, and the "shining mark" showing no disposition to recede, it was evidently to be a case of the "survival of the fittest."

The plane above proved to be a one-man machine, so that the contest for aim supremacy in this instance would be equal in that respect, a single pilot to each cruiser and a single gun to the fore of both.

Germany "opened the ball" with the first shot, but failed to score, for young America was not in the spot at which the aim was taken. The art of "fancy flying" was coming in handy.

Billy got a "bead" on his antagonist, but with no other result than to "hole a wing."

There was one thing, just about then, that our boy discovered—he had much the fastest machine of the two, an encouraging development of which the U. S. A. flyer immediately proceeded to take advantage.

He passed his antagonist at lightning speed, and, flash-like, reversed the direction of the flight by turning edgewise upon one wing, at the same time "letting loose" his machine gun at the German craft, the operator of which proved too slow of comprehension to offset the dashing maneuver by counter movement of swinging around for return fire.

Billy saw that he had the Boche pilot hopelessly on the "wobble," without the requirement of another broadside; indeed, the seconds were few before the "shot-up" machine was on the long tumble earthward, and the victor speeding away on a hunt for the all-around scrap in which his comrades were involved when the Bangor boy was on the way up.

That engagement, however, was no longer in progress, three out of the participating six of the German squadron backtracking in the dim distance, three that would be of no more assistance to the Kaiser, and, more grievous to relate, the original half-dozen Sammy flyers reduced to four, these survivors on the way to their own aerodrome.

There was nothing then for Billy to do but head that way himself. In the shanty he found his own particular pal, Henri, "Pure Grit" Patterson, Jimmy Bayles, and Dave Moffit. "Sam" Rhodes and "Charley" Sprague were not there. They had not "come back."

All of the talk behind the lines was of the tremendous drive that Hindenburg had just started against the Allied forces on the western front, the most colossal military effort of all times, and in the Swiss hut that night the discussion of the all-paramount news kept the aviators on edge until the commandant happened in with peremptory orders of retirement.

"Gee whiz!" was Billy's bunk-hour exclamation, for the special benefit of his chum, "if we could only have a look-down on that movement it would be the top-notch of our aeroplaning experience!"

"The biggest thing I know," agreed Henri.

Before the boys were more than half awake in the morning, they could have easily imagined by the racket with which the American gunners were opening the day that they were not far away from a "hot spot" after all.

The shelling that thoroughly roused the young scouts was certainly heavy, resulting in the complete destruction of enemy first- and second-line positions on a part of the sector at which the fire was directed.

Barry and Trouville had the first call out for an aerial tour of inspection over the Hun side of No Man's Land, which assignment, from its inception, carried the young pilots directly into an atmosphere where uncounted shells were whining like ripping silk and noisily bursting with mushrooms of coal black smoke. Even when clearing the explosives of the lower strata the pilots soon and several times heard sharp detonations so close to their machines that they could feel the concussion. They knew they were over the German Archies, and, so, riskily assured that what they wanted to find out was below for the looking.

Though the shells continued for awhile to burst near enough to give the young aviators considerable of a bumping, they managed to locate the points where the Prussians were using the rock crushers and concrete mixers in the construction of new field boxes opposite the American front. A couple of Hun cruisers lifted for contention with the U. S. A. flyers, but the latter, out this time for information and not for "blood," did not stop to fight, making it their business to get home as quickly as they could.

Following the "spotting" excursions of our boys and other aviators during the day, a raid of German positions was later undertaken by American and French troops under the cover of darkness as a misty haze began to roll in over the hills facing the U. S. A. lines on that particular portion of the sector.

From an observation station high in a treetop, Billy and Henri watched the artillery preparation. It began soon after dusk, orange bursts of flame where the American guns were firing in certain places in the wood round about. From the hillsides across the valley the German guns retaliated. For more than half an hour the brilliant bluish-white flash of their guns was like a jumping electric spark here and there. Soon the reports of the explosives became a deafening roar, which rolled in from everywhere as the guns, far and near, came into action.

This was the time for the barrage. From the spot where the shells fell a constant red glow showed through the darkness. At the same time the German guns increased their fire.

As the barrage lifted, the roar became quiet just at the moment the Americans and French went over the top.

Soon nearly all the heavy firing ceased and almost immediately the staccato rattle of machine guns and automatic rifles began. Occasionally rifle fire broke in, and then a more pronounced period of quiet.

The young scouts, held in rapt attention during the exciting period of noise and action, could not stand the lull in fixed perch.

They made short work of sliding down the tree trunk, and keyed up to the idea of going "over the top" themselves!

CHAPTER XII

A NIGHT RAIDING ADVENTURE

WHEN the young scouts reached and crossed the American first line they were not long in coming up with the stretcher-bearers accompanying the raiding party, and later mingling with the main body of invaders, all then mud-stained and some smeared with blood. A number of enemy trenchmen had been shot while they were trying to get away, and others killed by American shells.

Billy and Henri were close behind a Sammy soldier when the latter discovered and challenged a German who had placed himself between the first and second lines with an automatic rifle. The Hun turned to draw a revolver, when the American promptly "downed" him. At almost the same moment a gray-garbed figure partly arose from a shell hole nearby and drew "bead" on the youngster who had been so quick on the trigger. The menacing pistol sounded its whip-like crack, but the bullet did not follow the line of aiming—it was wasted in upshoot, for the reason that two lithe shapes had leaped from the shadows in tiger-like springs and hurling with unerring precision and baseball force hastily moulded spheres of clay, one catching the would-be killer smack between the eyes and the other forcibly providing him with a mouthful of mud.

Young Trouville had a record back of him as a crackerjack shortstop, and that Barry partner of his was once counted a "thrower from Throwersville" in the job behind the bat.

The comrade who thus escaped a "chunk of lead" (he, by the way, was a New Yorker), finished the business of quieting the fellow with slaying intent, and twisted a queer little grin in contemplating the life-savers when they were better revealed in the lurid light of a flame-burst occasioned by the blowing up of a dugout.

"I'll bet my hat," he remarked, "that you chaps weren't far from a major league before you signed this contract."

With the raiders now moving back from their successful invasion, the lads lost sight of the new friend, but hoping to "run across" him again at some future time.

"This work is a bit out of our line," said the Bangor boy to his pal, as they picked their way through the entrenchments, "but, believe me, it keeps the blood warm."

When the young scouts paused for a few moments on a ground elevation near the tree they had lately occupied as a lookout convenience, Henri called attention to the black overhead, gazing westward, saying:

"Something there, Buddy, in 'our line.'"

That "something" was a showing of a few moving stars—the red and white lights of French planes —here and there a burning fuse high in the heavens, like a particularly brilliant greenish star, little sparkles now and then of bursting shrapnel shells and occasionally a brilliant winking like a spark of a wireless coherer where a mitrailleuse was at work.

Somewhere "there" German airmen were night-raiding a town, and, perhaps, the redder glow that suddenly lighted the sky marked the fate of at least one of the raiders.

As the boys, in the graying dawn, were viewing the shanty headquarters, an enemy aeroplane was crossing the line at an altitude of 20,000 feet, the operator shutting off his motor and volplaning low in the obscurity of the early morning darkness, dropping another dose of the new style bombs, which exploded before they reached the ground, scattering clouds of mustard gas—which, heavier than air, slowly settled, spreading as it did so. The American gas officers, immediately detecting the presence of the poison by a reddish blue glare, were signaling for the men to put on their masks.

Billy and Henri applied "full steam" in their haste to respond to call for repelling service aloft, but Patterson and Bayles were having their turn in orders, and the flying twins were thus compelled to act as ground viewers of their comrades' attempt to "fix" the marauder. It was, however, another case of "no luck," for the German had a speed limit but little short of chain-lightning, and he used it to the best advantage for himself.

Our boys, though they did not get into the morning "chase," after all, really not fit for best endeavor, owing to lack of rest the night previous, had their flying call when daylight again merged into darkness, and, as an incident, "got wise" to another brand-new trick of the wily Boches.

The latter had been finding out that they were no match for the Allied flyers by day, though possessing some remarkable individual pilots and some wonderful machines. So of late, with the honors in air fighting by day incontestably with the Allies, the German aerial operators were making it their job in the daytime to observe and run away if they could, and only at night to go on raids.

The Allies, in consequence, were also and likewise increasing their operations at night. As the commandant to whom Billy and Henri looked for direct authority put it, according to childhood formula, "What goes up must come down." When word came that the Boches have started on a raid the Allied planes go up. The German aerodrome must be lighted, so its planes may land in safety.

Then the Allied bombers tear it to pieces with their explosives. The aerodromes are moved often, but are likewise bombed often.

Our Young Aroplane Scouts, as before intimated, were booked for a "tearing up" expedition that very night, having been "dead to the world" for six or seven hours in slumbering occupancy of their bunks.

The enemy aviators were especially in need of rebuke on the occasion for their after-dark activities, and Barry and Trouville heard summons to join with other daring spirits in putting a damper on the exhibit.

For the once, however, the outgoing outfit with destroying intent encountered a baffling proposition in locating illuminated spots from which the Teuton planes popped into the air. And they were "popping" just the same as usual, but the wherefrom this time a matter of obscurity.

The fact was, the cunning Prussians were rising from underground hangars—something new to even the foxy lad from Maine and his equally well-posted pal.

This bit of conception caught the young scouts unawares in passage over the concealed wide tunnels from which the Hun planes started, and if the enemy machines were to be reached it was by the hunt and hustle method, for they were flying too high nowadays, or, rather, "nowanights," for the searchlight or the shell barrage to get them. In this the raiders had all the advantage, for the defending planes must carry lights as a protection against attack by their own folk.

It so happened that the Kaiser airmen this night were indulging their new squadron formation in a raid on the towns on the French-American front—flying in squads and maneuvering by signal like a troop of cavalry. Three formations were engaged, apparently, and they flew from different directions. One would swoop in, drop its bombs, execute a half turn, and get out again. Half an hour later the next flotilla registered in.

Billy, Henri and another aviator by the name of "Peg" Strothers "got in the road" of one of these squads at a time when the raiding "bunch" had just unloaded their bomb supply on a town below, starting a few fires, and were on the getaway route.

After some "blind shooting" Strothers took "the drop," and his comrades quickly noted that the velocity of the fall, figured by the light on the disappearing machine, was hardly indicative of a "crash," but certainly confirming the belief that "Peg's" plane had, at least, been driven out of control.

Some French airmen immediately engaging the Hun aerial squad a little further on, our young scouts themselves took the chance of landing in some of the ground spaces illuminated by the bomb-created blazes on the outskirts of the town attacked.

The boys were not proposing to quit the scene of

trouble until they had relieved or realized their anxiety as to the landing fate of their gallant companion, a Massachusetts lad, and a true blue pal.

In the confusing downlook of black and red—night and fires—Billy had a close call of collision with a tall chimney, but righted in time to ground safely, within a few yards of where Henri had alighted.

The flying twins set out forthwith to look for Strothers, which search, happily, was not to be extended or extensive. Indeed, it was the hunted one who saw the hunters first, looking out from the center of a huddle of townspeople who had ventured into the open after the explosive scare had been reduced by a period of silence.

"This way, fellows," was the outcry of "Peg," "if you want to see the ninth wonder of the world, which is me. Couldn't shake me, could you, bully boys?"

"Came to save the pieces, anyway," laughingly rejoined the Bangor lad, "and mighty glad to find them altogether. What's the matter with the 'junk'?" the speaker pointing to the stranded aeroplane.

"Paralysis of the propeller," stated Strothers,

"aggravated by a German pill. Got a piece of string in your pocket?"

This conversation, in pure Yankee tongue, was Greek to most of the surrounding auditors, but the talking participants were no less objects of respectful admiration.

An urchin in a flapping coat, six times too large for him, just then shuffled into the circle with the almost breathless announcement that in broad translation—"more men birds come down over there."

"Over there" proved to be on the other side of the high chimney that Billy had failed to knock down.

True it was that more birdmen were down—two more—and both were Germans, with machines plugged in running parts by the French defensive flotilla in the aerial combat which had been going "hot and heavy" during the previous ten or fifteen minutes.

When the American aviators, leading the crowd to the landing place of the Hun pilots, faced the enemy flyers in the red glow emanating from a still-burning warehouse nearby, Billy sounded a note of recognition at sight of the foremost figure of the pair:

"If it isn't Conrad, I'm the king of Ballyhoo!"

"Conrad" was the Teuton high driver that the Bangor boy had once upon a time given a long slide with a broken arm at the end of it, and who, while the young scouts were prisoners in a hostile camp, had intensely desired to reduce the Barry family by one.

The Boche airman, too, evidently had a long memory as well as a peppery disposition, for he knew his former successful antagonist at first glance, and, despite the odds against him, as quick as a cat produced a revolver from his hip, getting a "level" on Billy which would have carried a bullet pretty straight into the breast of that youth when the trigger finger worked.

That deadly pressure, however, was never applied, for, by the display of remarkable agility on the party of such a heavyweight, and a sixty-year-older, the town blacksmith intervened with a short-arm jolt that instantly made the weapon-wielder "forget" his purpose.

"You're some slugger, my friend," remarked young Barry, in his best French, to the iron-armed forgeman, who continued his forcible rebuke by shaking the glaring and dazed Conrad like a dice-box.

When the prisoners had been turned over to French guardsmen just arriving on the scene, the U. S. A. trio proceeded to "doctor" Strothers' machine.

It developed, when the flying three returned to their own aerodrome in the very early morning, that whatever excitement had attended their night adventure, it was not a marker to the spirit elevation then prevailing in the American camp.

CHAPTER XIII

SELECTED SENTINELS AT DANGER POINTS

It was about four a. m. when the three aviators "pulled in," and with passing view of the greatest activity throughout the zone where the American troops were quartered. Heavily loaded motor trucks were rumbling over the roads, and marching men, horses and artillery—seemingly endless processions, some of which were miles long. The Star Spangled Banner was going to float beside the French and English flags in the plains of Picardy!

There was unbounded enthusiasm when Americans passed French troops at various times, the poilus waving and cheering.

The young scouts forgot all about the sleepless hours of their aerial expedition amid the scenes attendant upon the great movement to the front, eagerly anticipating participation in the Allied effort of resisting in augmented strength the onpush of the gray hordes treading gory lanes between their own piled-up, countless dead.

Every aviator in the command with which Billy and Henri were identified was at high tension, awaiting any special orders that might, at any minute, come the way of the flying force.

Our boys had the advantage of most of the others, owing to more intimate knowledge of the surrounding country and, too, far beyond the limit of the territory which could be traversed in the longest single march in any direction. They had been "there" before, meaning almost everywhere that the military maps of the warring zones of northern France could show.

Another airman in the squadron that had baffled the figuring of the experts as to the law of average in the perilous profession, and, too, a veteran also with a far traveling record along the high lines, was "Pure Grit" Patterson.

And so here was a trio who hoped for the first "go ahead" job on the strength of varied experience and as topography experts.

If the major in charge of the squadron that morning escaped the vision of the three pair of eyes, it could only have been accomplished by that officer crawling into a cave!

The "shanty crowd," or what was left of them,

along about noon "rigged up" a lunch in their chosen quarters, and having a talk among themselves as to fighting prospects.

A voice at the door, however, so far superseded in interest the sounding of their own tongues that the little company were instantly silent listeners to the say of the man looking in—and the especially expectant Barry, Trouville and Patterson also delayed halfway the very act of transferring food from hand to mouth.

The summons brought the first-named to standing position—he was named to report at headquarters.

"Remember the brothers in distress," was the jocular appeal of Jimmy Bayles, "and don't forget to write while away."

This chap, Bayles, as his comrades often claimed, would have difficulty in being serious at his own funeral!

Both Henri and "Pure Grit" gave the jester the rebuking eye, for they had no approval of anything that threatened a break in the "combination," even temporarily.

If Billy was listed to "go out," it meant, just now, something more than the usual "side trip."

"See you later, fellows," hastily remarked the Bangor boy, as he turned for a second in the doorway before continuing pursuit of the quickly departing orderly.

The Maine youth found the aviation commandant in conference with one of the chief directing powers of the military movement then in continuing progress, and stood at attention, at a little distance, until Major Hall, the squadron head, faced about and beckoned the young scout to come forward.

"You, I understand," said the one of higher command, directly addressing Billy, and appraising the lad with a questioning look, "have been flying around these parts for some time; in fact, are pretty well acquainted with the lay of the land?"

"Have been in the air service quite awhile, general," stated Billy, "and for a considerable period navigating over French territory."

The soldier leader turned to a map that covered the table at which he was sitting, and spotted with thumb-tacks that marked a routing study.

"Lend an eye here, young man," requested the officer, planting an index finger on one of the spots of the outline. "Know that place?"

The young scout leaned over to inspect the designated point.

At this time other members of headquarters staff had joined the council at the table.

"I sure do, general," finally announced Billy, when he had mentally noted the name of the town and its particular location on the map. "My flying partner and I one time came very near getting a finishing jolt in that neighborhood."

"You think then that you and your 'flying partner' could not fail in reaching that point without deviation, and would certainly recognize it when you got there?"

"As sure as the sun shines, general," confidently asserted the Bangor boy.

"That does not apply as good insurance this week, I fear," remarked the general with a smile, glancing out of the window at a much- traveled and very muddy road stretching away to the north. "But, I must concede that it is in the schedule for the sun to shine occasionally, so I will take it as your bond."

"I believe we are not mistaken in fixing this crossing as the probable point of interference."

The last remark was addressed to the staff officers roundabout.

Various replies indicated one agreement as to this.

"Well, we must rely on the advance report of this knowing young airman to some extent before we can put it down as sure and certain."

The general was again giving Billy the "once over."

"There's 'luck in odd numbers, sir,'" ventured that youth; "one might have an accident, but if there were at least three on the trip, chances would better warrant somebody getting back."

The Bangor boy was getting in a wedge for Henri and "Pure Grit."

"Oh, Major Hall here will arrange the details," said the general, "and, no doubt, satisfactorily. The best way is the way that gets results."

The major, it developed, was inclined to accept Billy's plea as the "right stuff," and one Henri Trouville and one "Pure Grit" Patterson were not slow in applauding the favorable decision when they heard of it!

Young Barry, practically in command of the special expedition of reconnaissance, received his definite instructions soon after the official interview, and, for surety of accomplishment, in turn imparted them to the comrades who were to accompany him.

They were charged with the duty of proceeding aloft, in direct line of travel, for the designated and suspected danger point, there and thereabouts to maintain ceaseless and wide-range aerial vigil over all the roads converging in the vicinity, and at the first sighted development of any considerable concentration or advance of enemy troops to track back like blue blazes with the warning words to the forward marching army of Uncle Samdom.

The three airmen vested with this responsibility had never an idle moment in contemplation of what they were expected to do, hardly less of a hustle than they might anticipate in the strenuous hours to come. It was essential that their flying gear should be perfectly "shipshape," as the saying is, every bit of mechanism tuned and tested to meet the requirements of long-sustained flights.

The details of preparation were hardly completed when the assisting hangar workers made way for the major's approach with the departing command.

Like disturbed quail in the stubble, the aviation trio were instantly up and away.

The pilots in their first bolting and some time thereafter looked down upon roads that for miles in every direction were choked to the utmost with every conceivable traffic of war—solid miles of American fighters coming from all points of the compass to join other forces bound on the same mission as those which had already passed—steadily streaming, brown-topped U. S. A. wagons, camouflaged guns and caissons—the new snap movement of a fighting instead of a training army.

About the only question expressed below as to destination was in the song being whistled and warbled by the Sammy boys in the transport vehicles— "Where Do We Go from Here?"

By and by the aviators had more time to look ahead, less activity underneath, and some extra pressure of memory on the part of the guiding spirit of the occasion, the flyer from Maine, who had sharp eyes peeled for one-time familiar landmarks in this speedy dash across country.

The "center spot of the web of roads" was the object of Billy's incessant scrutiny, and he remembered the town as a collection of red roofs with an uplift in the middle of a "funny-shaped" tower.

There was no telling, though, what, in the meantime, Boche shells might have done to that tower.

The dusk period of the day was nearing, and a storm cloud brooding closely overhead, which time and weather conditions were growing inducements for a "nesting period" at first favoring opportunity.

To the followers of Billy's lead a few minutes later it was evident, by lowering flight, that the head flyer had made a "find," and, Henri, in particular, owing to kindred knowledge in the premises, was able to anticipate the observation of the guide.

The sought-for locality was in sight, a scant mile to the fore, and the Bangor boy was clipping altitude to impress identity upon a friendly population.

This precaution was less of necessity when all of a sudden a "reception committee" appeared in the air to receive "credentials" or "repel boarders," as the case might be—two French planes and one of the British brand.

The incoming aviators made showing quick enough to avoid "unpleasant argument," even though the daylight was about gone at the time of meeting, and the Allied brethren flocked together in the "comedown."

"This seems to be a busy corner this evening," remarked the Bangor boy as he passed the "glad hand" to the nearest Tricolor representative at the landing place.

"And for good reason, no doubt," was the response, the English of it here given.

Henri was talking French in a streak to the other native of the soil on which they were standing, while "Pure Grit" had "hooked up" like an old friend with the Briton.

Patterson was saying, as the airmen grouped, "I guess the Allies are pretty near all here now."

"A working majority, at least," laughed young Barry.

Then the rain came down in torrents, and shelter was in demand for both men and machines.

"Mighty fine chance for the Boches to steal a march on us," said Billy, as he stamped the mud from his shoes after the job of getting the aeroplanes under some sort of cover was completed and the aviators were long-stepping it through the downpour toward inviting roof protection for themselves at the town hall.

The French airman hurrying alongside of the young scout no doubt intended some kind of reply, but for the startling interruption of a tremendous shell crash at the other end of the main street.

As one man the six runners stopped in their tracks.

"Gee whiz, that was a sounder!"

This exclamation by the Bangor boy.

CHAPTER XIV

MADE NEW MARKS ON THE MAP

"WONDER if that's a warrant for our warning retreat?" questioned "Pure Grit," in attitude of listening for another explosive shake-up.

The French aviator, who had been chumming with Henri, and lately from Paris, made quick response to the query.

"As like as not," he confidently advised, "the firing gun which sent that shell is many a mile away. I heard a burst not long ago that was given cause seventy miles distant. When we were aloft this afternoon there was not an artillery wheel set up as far as the strongest glass could reach, and no time since to reach ordinary range. No need, comrade, for us to act as alarmists this night."

"Right you are, my lad," properly maintained the Briton, "the Boche crowd haven't broken this way yet. They're still in the very dim distance, according to last observation. A little unsight-unseen target practice, that's all."

"Just enough to spoil somebody's sweet sleep," suggested Billy, indicating with sweeping gesture the various collections of townfolk along the stone-flagged thoroughfare.

"But not sufficient to spoil my appetite," put in Henri. "Show me food, if there's any round here."

There being no successor of the big noise, renewed calm operated to bring well-disposed inhabitants of the town to the front with ample satisfaction for the "inner man" demands of the Ally aviators, accepted by their hosts in the imagined rôle of veritable guardian angels, or, at least, as representatives thereof.

With comforting blankets, and dry spots on which to lay them, the air sentinels of the morrow were complacent gentlemen of leisure, while the night wind sighed its utmost and the rain splashed on the tiled roof above.

A really rising sun, about the first showing in forty-eight hours, was splintering its rays through the diamond points of a high and wide window, and full in the face of the sleeper at the furthest end of the bunk row, which proved to be the Bangor boy, who never liked to get up early, but generally had to, this being one of the occasions of peremptory demand.

Awakened by the golden bath on his ruddy countenance, Billy had the immense satisfaction, as recently appointed leader, of immediately hauling his pal out of his soft blanket roll and, also, of applying the "hot foot" to the snoring Patterson.

This playful commotion had the effect of an eye-opener upon the rest of the aviation company, and "all hands" were immediately active in preparing for the scouting operations of the day.

They well knew that the night had brought no nearer any hostile force, or their rousing would have been hastened by a trusty sentry in the tower, who, since the first faint break of the morning, had been scanning through a powerful binocle the surrounding country.

The shrewd Barry lad had left nothing to chance.

With the speed he had at command it was feasible to take a long trail in order to find out from what source and at what present starting station the Huns were contemplating the suspected blockade of this keystone position.

The unexpected aid for reconnoitering work of the three additional aviators made it possible to cover far greater range of territory, and at the same time to make better accounting in the event of aerial attack while flying investigation was in progress.

A thorough understanding, however, was established between the U. S. A. trio of pilots that it must never happen that all should participate in a single engagement, if forced to that extremity, in order to insure one living messenger for the solemnly charged duty of bringing back any advices of vital import.

"I know," said Billy, "that the assignment of 'playing safe' is not to the liking of anyone of us, but, when dodging means a whole lot more than taking your medicine front face, this rule goes without question. If two of us run into a fight, the third must 'hold his horses.' With the help of our scrappy friends here that'll be enough for a showing, anyhow."

"Pure Grit," tinkering with a belt-knuckle that would not "take hold" the way he wanted it to, paused for a second or two to let his imagination present a picture of himself showing the "white

feather" to a Boche pilot. But he realized that the
Bangor boy's precaution was due to strict observance, leaving Patterson the lone hope of not being
the rear guard if a shindy broke out.

Far away to the south, American soldiers were
in forward march through miles of tree-lined roads
just faintly green with newly budding spring
leaves—and that they should walk not unawares into
the jaws of a gigantic steel trap, much depended
upon these winged rangers in advance—veritably the
"eyes" of the army.

The U. S. A. flyers took the direct westerly
course in their morning patrol, while the French and
British aviators proceeded north and east. The objective of the first three was fixed at the dim, dark
line of a distant wooded section, the one concealing
barrier to the vision in that direction, and, save a
chain of hills rounding the open to the southwest,
about the only place that any camouflage could be
perpetrated.

Fan-shape was the formation of the aerial approach of the timberland, "Pure Grit" leading at
the right, Henri at the left, and Director Barry in
the center and rear.

Over the tree-tops it was Patterson who made

the first discovery that the vicinity contained something more than a graveyard. A shell rocketed from some invisible battery, and so close to the passing machine that a few feet would have made all the difference in the world to the pilot. "Pure Grit," while up-nosing for a climb, had still another reminder that haste was worth while—and it was a sure thing that the ever-ready aviator applied all the curlycues known to his experience in correcting the impression that he was an easy mark.

Young Trouville, profiting by sight of the explosive reception accorded his comrade on the right angle, sought the sky-line with all the promptitude of a seasoned mariner in the face of a sudden squall, while Billy, the center-pin, side-wheeled along the outer edge of the forest, readily convinced that the woods or their background were full of big guns.

"Another look will be a plenty, I guess," he muttered to himself, going like a gull before a gale in his search for a crossing point with more of a view under it.

The Bangor boy took to the opening lightning fast when he found it, a valley break in the high growth, and a whole lot of development in a wide and timber-free area coming under the eager inspection of the young scout. Germans were there, and a host of them, too, in marching order, infantry and artillery corps, a mass of compact formation, ready to take the road eastward, which, with broad and firm surface, was also now revealed, skirting the southern extremity of the wood.

Billy knew then all there was to know, and his next strain of vision was to locate his flying comrades, amply assured that they had, in further advance, fully reviewed the situation, from the angles they were pursuing, and, naturally, anticipated that Henri and "Pure Grit" would swing around in wide detour for return to the cross-roads rendezvous, the revelation of the past quarter-hour leaving only the incentive of a united effort to win back to their own command with the word which would thrill and set alert the serried ranks of the forward-moving U. S. A. host.

But just at that time neither Trouville nor Patterson were in position to change flight as they pleased, or as wise heads dictated. Instead of veering away, north and south, this aviation pair were on a drive which tended to contract the distance between them—a drawing together enforced by the flanking interference of a half dozen or more Hun planes suddenly bobbing up, in equal division, at both ends of the wood, and still another block to escape in skyward direction in the shape of a couple of armored air-cruisers coming in at great elevation from the hill region.

Billy noted that the U. S. A. machine at the right was already spitting fire—the "human hurricane" demonstrating his objection to the crowding of the enemy planes upon his right of way—and directly the watching pilot's own particular pal at the left duplicated the Patterson performance in turning loose with the lead at the nearest flying foe.

According to the special starting agreement, the Bangor boy had drawn the blank which kept him out of the fight, and, besides, with attention soon diverted from the "come together" over the wood by the promptly introduced effort of anti-aircraft guns on the ground to "clip the wings" of the onlooker, forcing the latter to get out of range in a hurry.

Another backward look, however, gave the Barry lad a heart-leap of joy, for he saw that his comrades had somehow or other broken through the buzzing ring of would-be destroyers, and, side by side, streaking it northward. This was Billy's cue to "make tracks" for the crossroads town, not then knowing of the further good fortune of the companion aviators in being reinforced by the three Allies, who had been scouting on their own hook in the north, and which resulted in an air battle that "crashed" two of the pursuing planes, with the others outdistanced.

Twenty minutes later the flying six were together again in front of the old town hall, and putting their aeroplanes in condition for another long flight being made to serve as the exercise necessary to straighten out the "kinks" of body confinement in contracted space.

As to rest, the airmen had but little of that, and that little enlivened by continued shelling from big guns afar—a reminder of what might be expected in increased accuracy and effect if the gray artillerymen got a chance at any moving columns passing that way.

"Well, brothers," said Billy to the French and British aviators as he stood by his machine just before the parting moment, "we're booked to go different ways to-day, but it won't be long, I hope, until the whole push of us will be traveling in one direction, into the big fight, and it can't be too quick to suit me."

"Ditto!" cried "Pure Grit," shaking hands all around with the pilots who had come to the aid of Trouville and himself in the recent scrimmage. "We owe you something, fellows, and don't forget to present the bill at first sight when we hit the smoky row."

Henri and the plucky little aeroplanist hailing direct from Paris had the last word together after the others were under way to take wing.

"If you get to Amiens" (the then storm center), "tell 'em that we're coming too."

With this the U. S. A. lad hastened to overtake the pair already on the high line and heading for their command, primed with information of the greatest value to the directing power at American headquarters.

Billy Barry presented his widest smile to the major when the latter lent a hand to the young scout's dismounting at the home hangars.

"Got something under your helmet?" questioned the officer.

"All that grew there, sir, and then some," was the reply.

"Come along, then, and relieve the pressure," invited the commandant.

"With my main witnesses, major, if you please," suggested the Bangor boy, turning to Trouville and Patterson.

"Sure," said the flying chief.

That evening there were some new marks on the military map!

CHAPTER XV

THE HOTTEST SPOT ON THE CONTINENT

OUR Young Aeroplane Scouts at last were realizing upon their oft-expressed desire of getting close to the great battle making lurid each and every day of the advancing spring in northern France—that titanic conflict with which the fronting fields ran red to the very knees of combatants numbered almost beyond comprehension and counting.

Veterans by experience though they were, our boys had scarcely claim to being hardened as witnesses of such terrific slaughter nor restrain that first shudder at the shambles it created.

Uncle Sam's fighting men had reached the British battle zone, and with the rest Billy Barry and Henri Trouville. The U. S. A. troops had greeting of intense enthusiasm, when these overseas pioneers, a battalion of infantry, came swinging along the road into a powder-warmed sector after an all-night march that began on the anniversary of America's declaration of war. The dusty uniforms and unshaven faces of the incoming soldiers showed that they had been long on the road.

The flying twins were but a few hours in the vicinity of an important stretch of the front when they "ran across" quite a number of British and French airmen who, like themselves, had survived active participation in the earlier day campaigns of the world war, and some formerly known to our boys even in fields as remote as the Balkans.

One likable chap, in particular, a Verdun veteran, with a long string of daring exploits and hairbreadth escapes on his "score card," indulged in a whoop of recognition upon sighting Billy and Henri, while the latter pair were giving "all eyes" to some of the furious German onslaughts and the counter "rolling back" process effectively applied by the Allies.

"Never lost where there's a shuffle," was the shouted welcome of George Lorry, "and it's just as natural as an apple tree to see you fellows at the hottest spot now on the continent."

"We'll admit, George," observed the Bangor boy, when the young scouts had done their share of glad greeting, "that this is something of a furnace. How does the aeroplaning job fit in, old top?"

"You'll see, my hearties," exclaimed Lorry; "it's never near zero, even upstairs, believe me!"

"There's a bunch that's sure paying the price," interrupted Henri, looking out from the high ground position behind the lines. "What a killing!"

The speaker referred to the casualties being inflicted by the thousands upon a Teuton advance of close formation, in one place in as many as seven waves, each wave ten men deep and one hundred yards apart.

"I've seen a lot of bloody battlefields in my time," declared the one-time hero of Verdun, "but since the first strike by Hindenburg at this front it's been the biggest short-time tear-up that ever hit my vision."

Our boys were not disposed to contradict Lorry relative to the size of the conflict, in continuous raging, after witnessing even that portion of it within seeing distance of the aviation center, where they awaited orders for their first fighting trip hereabouts, in the speediest kind of company.

When "Pure Grit" and Jimmy Bayles arrived a day later, in advance of another American battalion of infantry, Billy and Henri had assurance for the "human hurricane" and his companion that there would be "plenty doing" for the air contingent when the then prevailing mist and rain should clear away.

"Some cracking good lads are riding for the Allies here," further asserted Billy, "and it's our business to keep our records from getting rusty when we go out with them."

Patterson showed his slow smile, remarking:

"Oh, for that, my hearty, we'll do our little bit and our largest best."

Nobody came forward to challenge the U. S. A. boy in regard to so modest a statement.

George Lorry had passed his word to the four newcoming aviators that when he next went out to "take issue" with the Huns from the topside they were going along, and George had something of a "say" in the veteran air squadron as a flight leader, able to vouch for the quartette as the "real stuff" when it came downright to aeroplane gunning or effective bomb manipulation.

Only twenty-four hours previously this "go to it" pilot, with a number of other flyers of the same caliber, had routed a German battalion by efficient bomb planting, and the same outfit later in the day produced many cases of enemy panic by machine-gun fire, shooting simultaneously from their aero-planes.

There came the morning with the mist and moist-ure departed but the atmosphere rimmed with layers of smoke, where the great guns were belching tre-mendous introduction of a famous three days of violent and unceasing artillery bombardment. Then the advancing of the first gray foe to the near recep-tion of a storm of bullets. Gaps appeared in these oncoming lines in many places, some of them large where machine guns chewed through. Still the Ger-man waves came on, without firing a single shot—just advancing.

This was a point of action viewable through the constantly fixed binocles of the flying men, who tensely awaited the slipping of the authoritative leash that held them to earth.

The scythe-like stream of lead from the machine guns had no abating, and yet no halting of the on-moving mass. Again and again the fire-mown lanes were closed by the living re-forming over the dead and dying.

Then was the air alive with winged agents of war, those mighty factors of deadly execution in field operations—five—ten—now twenty cruisers aloft, carrying heavy weight of explosives, to be employed in fearful havoc by the fearless mariners of the boundless ether.

Four in a row planed the lately arrived members of the "shanty" crowd, grimly resourceful in such missions and without a tremor in their makeups.

The charging aeroplanes carried bomb showers into the very heart of the massed attack, taking fearful toll along the trail they blazed, and using, also, machine guns with telling effect.

Billy and Henri were in the far front of the death-dealing aircraft when the combined drive had produced a turning movement of the gray soldiery in the angle at which it was directed, and by this time widely separated from Patterson and Bayles, with whom they had started, side by side.

By the forward sweep of their high-powered cruisers, the young scouts, at the altitude then maintained, were in dangerous proximity to enemy battery points, and quite too often for comfort the pilots felt the shock of concussion above and below, with the fabrics that bore them rocking like cradles in the shell-storms that rent the upper reaches.

Having struck their blow en masse, the members

of the aviation squadron were backtracking, singly or in pairs, and scattering in every direction, getting out of reach, as they could, of retaliatory long-range gunnery on the part of the Hun artillerymen.

Our boys lost no time in clearing the troubled atmosphere where they had been drawing all they wanted of violent vibration, and in a decidedly short period put several thousand more feet between them and the battlefield below.

The young scouts were the last in at the aviation center, which accounted for all of the twenty participating planes, save three, lost somewhere in the vortex far afield. "Pure Grit" and Jimmy had been "jarred" to some extent, as the former stated it, but "still alive and kicking."

"Couldn't miss 'em," was an additional remark of the "human hurricane," "and everything counted as a 'flock shot.' Sure it was a run for everybody's money."

In the off-duty period behind the lines Billy and Henri were, as usual with them, interested spectators of that which strikes the imagination vividly, namely, the immensity of the movements of the troops and the order with which these are regulated. Traffic directors stand day and night at every cross-road, giving directions so that every vehicle and cannon can reach its proper station with clock-like regularity. The whole scheme is superintended by special officers who have sat in small cabins for days without a moment's rest, receiving directions from the various staffs and transmitting them along the line. Any vehicle breaking down is immediately ditched; otherwise the whole scheme would come to naught and the battle array be endangered.

"Some system, old top," commented the Bangor boy to his pal, "and though we've seen a lot of this sort of thing I never get tired of wondering how they do it."

The Maine youth was soon to have something else to "wonder" about—a case of marveling how Henri and himself got out with whole skins from a fiery tangle in which they were embroiled the following afternoon.

While taking the place of cavalry for reconnoissance work, a select number from the aviation squadron were covering ground space at points, in some instances, quite a long ways from their own aerodromes, and it happened that Barry and Trouville, scouting in near company, a custom to which they adhered whenever possible, struck a down view of a retreat of the Allies from a position that had grown too hot to hold.

The retiring forces were making use of armored motor cars, fitted with machine guns, to harry their pursuers. One of these, which had been in close contact with the enemy throughout the first half of the day, became ditched, this misfortune immediately noted by the two flyers then overhead, who also saw the occupants leave the car and endeavor to pull the machine out of the mud, all the time subjected to severe rifle fire.

A machine gun was lifted and used against the foe until it jammed. Then the gunner seized a rifle and fired while his comrades continued effort to right the car.

The Germans were no further away than fifty yards at this time, and it was apparently "all up" with the gallant little company halted in the road.

Then a couple of factory-made meteors flashed their way groundward.

Not having been on a bombing expedition, traveling light, the young scouts were unable to hold high and lend aid to the comrades sorely beset by a downpour of explosives upon the menacing Huns, but the pilots, determined anyhow to intervene in the combat, took the dip which would give them range for machine-gun operation, and, also, at the same time, it may be stated, making of themselves excellent targets for return rifle fire.

This latter consideration, however, in the flush of fighting spirit, did not deter the intrepid airmen in their purpose of giving the Teutons "both barrels" from overhead and affording an extra opportunity for the assailed carmen to make a successful getaway.

The aeroplane diversion well served the intent of the flyers. While they were pumping lead into the enemy ranks, the motorists got the car in going order, and going, too, at a merry clip down the road —the aviators, having accomplished their daring design, fleeing, at even greater speed, by a sharp turn, over the open country in the direction of their own station, climbing fast as they proceeded.

Every rifleman at the fore of the baffled German crowd took a try at the receding cruisers, and that the drivers thereof escaped at least a stinging was something of a surprise to even these firm believers in their own luck, for some of the pellets whistled mighty close, indeed, to their ears, spattering against the plane bodies and in numerous places cutting through wings and rigging.

Nary a vital spot in either machine, though, got a "stopper," and not even a scratch inflicted upon the pilots. The latter had no sooner landed at the aviation base when George Lorry charged upon them with a bit of information which immediately put the late adventure in the back number class.

"We're going after that seventy-mile gun in the morning," advised the Verdun celebrity, "and if we hit it, it will sure make a "cyclopedia record' for Barry, Trouville and yours truly."

CHAPTER XVI

A BOMBING EXPEDITION

"THAT Frenchman, Lorry," said Billy to his chum, after the enthusiastic proposer of the gun hunt departed to have at least his tenth interview of the afternoon with the aviation commandant in regard to his scheme to put the long-range "Paris disturber" out of business, "talks 'Boston' now about as well as you do, and if we ever get down to the quiet life again, I'm going to invite him to tie up with our firm."

"He'd win in most any job," agreed Henri, "and I'd pick him as one of the men to drive Barry planes across the ocean when that service is established."

The young scouts, despite the fact that theirs was a continuous juggle with death, never talked any other way than of life long lasting.

They had already forgotten even the narrow squeak of the hour just past.

Of Lorry's plan of action our boys were not then advised, but the idea had its strong appeal to these adventurous spirits, and they were more than eager to see the thing through. George came around in the night to tell them that the trip would carry the trio out of reach of the "big noise right around here" for a day or two, but with the inference that "we're likely to hit another hullabaloo most any time."

"We'll be packing some heavy blow-up stuff ourselves," he continued, "but won't take on the load at this end of the line. It's lightning express for the first leg of the journey."

"That's up to you, old top," conceded the Bangor boy. "Go ahead with your rat-killing, and we'll just go along to fill up the cracks."

"He's sure 'wise' to something," was Henri's musing comment when Billy and himself turned in for a bit of sleep—roaring guns to the contrary notwithstanding.

The youths had reason to anticipate that there would be a whole lot doing before they had another chance to snooze.

When next Lorry appeared he was "all buckled up" for flight, and while our boys were "getting outside" of hot coffee the hustling George was guessing weather prospects from an early morning standpoint.

"Good sailing, fellows," he presently announced. "By the way," added the speaker, "it's a wonder that that cannonading over in the west last night didn't loosen the foundations of all outdoors. Wasn't it fierce?"

Young Barry was compelled to state that he had not particularly noticed any unusual sound-burst, and his bunk-mate also plead guilty to the same degree of "deafness."

"Lay me out," exclaimed the questioner, "but you laddies have either very bad ears or a conscience apiece clear as crystal! That blasting awakened me, all right."

Which was some concession to the artillery action attending the Picardy engagements, when the man who made it had lived for months in the thunder-shaken atmosphere of Verdun!

Billy and Henri were inclined to surprise when they noted that the type of battleplanes drawn out for the flight lacked the explosive ballast that usually belonged to their equipment, then they remembered what Lorry had said about "loading" somewhere else.

An indication, too, that the same loading would be "for bear," as they say in the States.

"Pure Grit" and Jimmy were around at the start, and could not conceal that they were much aggrieved over the declared "cold deal" coming to them in regard to the special mission, about which these willing workers were all in the dark.

"Suppose we'll be invited to the funeral, if nothing else," growled Patterson as the three leaving aviators climbed into their machines.

"The next time, for you, old boy," were the last consoling words of the Bangor boy.

In a little over a half hour, the departing trio, flying at great height, had evidently reached the descending point contemplated by Lorry, for that worthy then began the drop movement through the clouds for better earth view and verification of the bearings he had in mind.

It was very soon apparent that the landing place for which George was guiding was a town in the center of an expanse of hill and valley and near a winding river; also that the center and immediate surroundings were occupied by French troops.

Lorry made the proper showing on the way down, and directly the airmen were enjoying the welcome accorded to friends. When the aerial expedition chief had had a talk with the commanding officer in the latter's town office, the reception took on additional warmth, and much interest was manifested as to George's ascertainment of the whereabouts of the mysterious engine of war which had been transcending all records of long range gunnery.

"Two of our flying patrolmen are responsible for the tip," explained Lorry, "and I'm pretty sure that they picked the right spot in what is called 'Castle Top,' a high point twenty-five miles west of here. The big cylinder, of course, is camouflaged, but I think we can find it easily enough. Give us the tear-up material, general, and we'll try to put it into the middle of the gun station."

"My comrades here," he continued, "have had a lot of experience in bomb work aloft, and I know a little something about it myself."

A "little something"—the speaker was a "regular terror" in boring holes in hostile ranks and territory!

With enough dynamite aboard to sink a man-of-war in twenty minutes the battleplanes resumed flight shortly after the noon hour, bound on a venture of destruction that, if successful, would set the wires flashing with messages of relief to the metropolis of France.

"If we don't succeed," Lorry had remarked just before starting for the distant hills, "it will be well worth while even to have tried."

George knew where he was going, anyhow, whatever the finding on arrival.

"Castle Top" was easy of recognition in the far look-down perspective, owing to its peculiar formation, and its natural arrangement of rock and tree into resemblance of that which gave the name to this elevation.

But discernment of what this hill concealed in its wooded growth and stony cavities demanded closer investigation to develop. To be sure if it had been a firing time of the great cylinder, believed to be mounted on this height, that would have settled the question of location in a tremendously effective manner.

However, it did not so happen that the seeking aviators were presented with such earth-shaking evidence of the near presence of a cannon with projectile casting force heretofore unknown.

The airmen had, then, to get near enough to the supposed gun station to penetrate the disguising methods of the cunning operators if there was to be any bomb-dropping on the Krupp marvel that might, at least, put it out of action for some time by destroying the sustaining base or "mixing up" the loading and range-finding mechanism.

Pilot Lorry was not at all backward in taking any chance, long or short, if it would eventually contribute to the success of the mission he was promoting. His companions had been selected by him because of the knowledge that they would not hesitate to compete with any example of daring venture.

George had shrewd surmise that if the biggest gun was there, some of lesser caliber would also be found, for use if emergency demanded, and some high-class gunners to work them.

And it would not be a far cry to guess that the protective facilities of "Castle Top" also included some fighting aircraft in underground hangars.

Altogether it was a sure thing that the would-be bombers went into close quarters with eyes wide open.

The intent of the trio was to "turn loose" their cargoes of "hot stuff" in a lump if the right mark showed up and then vamoose while the going was good.

Still traveling close to the cloud line, the airmen presently hovered directly over "Castle Top," with glasses trained on the rugged surface of the high ground. Then, circling lower and lower, the flying machines drew within easy eye distance of the hilltop.

Billy Barry had the luck to make the first mark-down of the concrete nest of the monster cannon, and at the same moment the intrusion of the aviators was resented from the black mouths of a dozen upturned muzzles lifting from the undergrowth on both sides of the hill; as by magic the place was alive with gray figures, the atmosphere ablaze with ascending gunfire.

Lorry and Trouville, getting the same revelation that had fixed the vision of the Bangor boy, joined the latter in letting go the destroying missiles with which the marauders were so plentifully supplied, a counter demonstration that turned things generally "upside down" in a ground radius of several hundred yards.

To save themselves a similar overturning experience, for the topside was becoming a veritable tempest of explosives, the pilots were forced skyward, using every ounce of motor power to get out of the way of the ever-increasing number of shells hurtling aloft.

Exactly the extent of the damage they had inflicted upon the mammoth gun-pit, the fast-climbing aviators had no means of knowing, but sufficient assurance that they had hit the right spot, and hit it hard.

Though now out of ordinary gun-range, the bombing trio had not seen the end of this adventure—they had stirred up a hornets' nest, and angry hornets are never inclined to gentle acceptance of any disturbing element. The Hun species is no exception to the rule—further evidenced in this instance by a new exhibit of stinging endeavor, the appearance in the upper reaches of a swarm of vengeful insects of the mechanical variety, motor driven and dangerous of contact.

The Ally flyers, rather well satisfied with their "tear-up" accomplishment, were not hankering for any half-dozen to one odds in an air fight just at that time, preferring, very likely, to again risk their lives when there was no practically sure thing against them.

Lorry, better posted than his companions in regard to this particular stretch of territory, kept in the van of the flight, and Our Young Aeroplane Scouts looked to the wily George for maneuvering directions that would serve to defeat the annihilating purpose of the hostile planes.

The leader of the getaway endeavor made choice of continuous upward course as a starter for his plan of avoidance, and, finally, aimed for darkening cloud billows then densely massing high in the northwest, this black banking ever and anon streaked by vivid flashes of lightning, with the dull rumble of thunder contributing to tempestuous aspect.

Apparently anticipating the objective of the diversion from rocketing tactics, the division of the Hun aerial squadron, which had sprung up from the chain of hills nearest to the driving line adopted by the foremost pilot of the Ally trio, combined in effort of interception, while the several other sections of the flying fleet at the rear buzzed in swift pursuit of Lorry and his comrades.

To outride both enemy planes and a gathering

storm was a contract to try the mettle of even such survivors of a hundred or more dallyings with fatal finishes as the three who were then once more playing the old game in opposition to the grim reaper.

The every-day sort of "century run" in the hour was plodding in comparison with the motor pressure being utilized by the guiding spirits of the threatened aircraft, charging into the dark envelopment of violent atmospheric disturbances and menaced on all sides by man-made destroying agents.

It was an uncertain toss-up now as to the outcome of the desperate situation!

CHAPTER XVII

OUTWITTED THE BOCHES

So close now the Hun planes, particularly the half-dozen essaying to "cut" the forward course of the madly driving Ally pilots, that any further loss of way by climbing would have resulted in the pocketing of the outnumbered cruisers in a whirling circle of wildly eager enemy operators, from which there could be no escape save by a miracle of prowess.

For every beating down of an assailing aircraft another would succeed, so numerous the hostile array sailing from all quarters to a common center —a surrounded air space, as anticipated by the Teuton collection, with easy prey in the middle.

But when the ring was rounded, it had nothing inside except atmosphere.

The "prey" had beaten the cordon by about three minutes, and somewhere in the cloud bank were dashing blindly through heavy layers of moisture, thunder shaken and criss-crossed by dazzling zig-zags of lightning.

Lorry had taken the "only way," and with our boys now on each side of the before leading plane, all going at equal speed, and all hoping for an early break from the enveloping elements.

Of little concern then was the German gang in the back stretches—the three cloud-pushers had the bulge on the Boches, if not on the storm environments, and if the gas in the tanks held out there was at least a fighting chance of finding the other side, or, maybe, the top of the inclement surroundings.

The relief, it developed, was presented by the "other side," into which clear area the fortune-favored trio presently raced, but considerably out of plumb, so to speak, with the line of travel that would carry them anyways directly in return to the French military base where they had taken on the "blow-up" stuff so effectively planted on "Castle Top."

A very inviting expanse of grassland below, and the fact that the machine which George was piloting had gone a bit "queer," impelled the expedition leader, after careful and assuring survey of the territory round about, to seek landing, followed, of course, by his comrades.

"Some tight squeeze, that," observed Henri, when the aviators had solid ground again under foot, referring to the thrilling experience just recorded.

"What's the odds s'long as we're happy?" smilingly queried Billy, an expression of eminent satisfaction with the existing condition.

"That's the way to talk," approved the Verdun veteran, about to busy himself as an inspector of the inside workings of his aeroplane. "I'd be willing to offer a joyful shout, in addition, if somebody would throw in an X-ray of the earth eruption we left on 'Castle Top.' Hope there's a red-hot spike in the old long-range contraption that'll hold it for awhile."

George did not have the disappointment then of knowing that if his party had been successful in putting out of commission one of the marvelous German guns that had been shelling Paris at a distance of seventy-six miles, nine more similar bombing applications would be necessary to choke the practice of far firing. Lorry's tip, however, had included only the location visited, and that place surely had its reminder of the call.

It has been related of the ten mammoth "shooting irons" possessed by the Teutons, that they had seen service as 15-inch naval guns, later refitted with inner tubes, which reduced the caliber to 9½ inches, the shells fired from them weighing 200 pounds, and a muzzle velocity of 6,000 feet per second attained. In the long-distance bombardment—a stupendous flight to figure—these guns were fired at an angle of 45 degrees, the shells rising to a height of between 25 and 30 miles or between 130,000 and 158,000 feet. The time consumed from muzzle to target is between one and one-half and two minutes, traveling, say, 25 miles high and 75 miles by straight line.

In the later language of Billy Barry, "some guns!"

When Lorry had found and repaired the flaw in the fabric that carried him, the next question was the choice of the most direct route to friendly lines and a base of supplies where petrol could be obtained in sufficient quantity to insure continuous flight in the long run to the aviation station back of the big battle front.

George was compelled to admit that the forced flight in the wrong direction had extended beyond any anticipation of his, and he did not exactly know how far would be the travel to reach friendly shelter and the aid desired.

"We'll go browsing, anyhow," he finally stated, "and maybe you fellows will recognize some of the country as we go along. If it isn't German it'll do, eh?"

"Listen to the Yankee from Paris," laughed the Bangor boy. "He's even lost the accent with which he lisped in childhood's happy hour."

"You'll be changing your tune," admonished Lorry, "if we don't get somewhere before the gas gives out."

If Billy Barry changed his tune when "somewhere" was sighted, it was not a "dead march" in which he indulged, for the sector into which the aeroplanes flew was occupied by Americans, intensely engaged in preventing the Boches from sharing any of the ground.

Indeed, the first view from aloft revealed a scene of terrific hand-to-hand fighting, the kind of action that most appealed to the Maine youth, and all the more a cause of inspiration in that the khaki-clad forces seemed to be having all the best of it.

The engagement the incoming aviators were witnessing was the German attempt to break through the American lines in the Toul vicinity. The Teutons that were hurled against the U. S. A. boys came full of bravado and arrogance, waving their rifles and shouting like mad, but they found more than they bargained for!

This time Pilot Barry led the way when the aeroplanes landed.

The airmen, it appeared, had arrived at a decidedly warm period, and as indicating the violence of the offensive Lorry was again inclined to declare that, comparatively speaking, the German artillery fire against the Americans was heavier than in any single engagement on the Verdun front at any time.

Yet with the coming of the morning after this heavy onslaught the U. S. A. main positions remained intact, and the overseas troops attacked and drove the enemy out of the old outposts which they had gained, thus breaking down an offensive which was believed to be the beginning of a German plan to separate the Americans and the French.

Our Young Aeroplane Scouts would have been very well suited by a longer stay with Uncle Sam's forces in this sector, but their own command was elsewhere, and Lorry was at their elbows, suggestive of early return to the other fighting zone to which they all were assigned.

Not long thereafter "Pure Grit" Patterson and Jimmy Bayles were welcoming their one-time "shanty" partners, with open ears for the story of the hazardous journey in which the listeners would have given almost anything to have been participants.

The next time out, though, the "human hurricane" and the other "left behind" were largely in evidence, when night-flying squadrons of the Allies dropped tons of bombs on hostile aerodromes. Barry and Trouville, too, had places in huge bombing machines, again, and over again, exemplifying the daily life of the airman, who continually battles on the edge of a precipice, while the many hands of war reach out to drag him down.

A word picture of this particular raid, as an example of some of the iron nerve requirements ordinarily, to the reader, perhaps, extraordinarily, demanded in aerial warfare:

About the great aerodrome the evening shades were falling and the mechanics were making their final inspection of the powerful bombing machines which shortly were to wheel their way across the fighting lines with their freight of explosives. Some day-flyers were returning from their trips, winging their way straight and true towards the aerodrome from all directions like mighty homing pigeons.

The night flyers were to go out as soon as the darkness had settled, and all of them had early dinners in the mess hall. Twelve of the big machines were to engage in the raid at hand, which meant that twenty-four of these clean-cut boys would soon be risking their lives over the inhospitable zone where the Germans watch and wait for the appearance of enemy aircraft. Among the number to pair this time in the bombing operations were Our Young Aeroplane Scouts, Patterson with Bayles, and Lorry with that lion of the upper paths, Gerald Mardo, who had recently figured in the daring and successful raid on factories in Mannheim, starting a conflagration that was visible for a distance of thirty-five miles.

A siren began its uncanny wailing somewhere outside, and a silence fell over the hall. One by one the twenty-four men separated themselves from their comrades and stole quietly from the room.

It was dark. A pale crescent moon struggled

bravely but ineffectively to clear away the gloom below. Strange, shadowy figures were flitting noiselessly about the grounds, and against the sky-line could be seen the blots which represented the great machines that stood waiting for their pilots and observers.

Off toward the east the sky quivered and glowed fitfully with the crimson flashes from a myriad guns, while the shrapnel hurled vicious flashes all along the line. It was toward these ominous beacons that the flight was going.

There was no delay. Time was valuable, for there were signs that mists might come at any time. Within five minutes the throbbing of a powerful engine began, a machine gun barked as the observer (it was Henri Trouville) tested the weapon, and then the plane glided swiftly away across the field and swept into the air, its little signal lights gleaming like stars. Another followed, and another, until the twelve had all embarked on their perilous voyage whose ending no one could prophesy.

CHAPTER XVIII

SAVED BY IRON NERVE

GRADUALLY the blinking eyes of the planes disappeared from the sight of the watchers at the aerodrome, all eyes of those on the ground strained towards the battle lines where the flights would cross.

Suddenly a stream of balls of fire began to mount high into the air over the trenches. The airmen had reached the land of hate and their punishment began in earnest.

The deluge continued, and the shrapnel flashed in ever-increasing numbers. German searchlights went peering through the clouds. One ray rested squarely on an over-riding plane, the machine guided by Billy Barry. It was a heartbreaking moment for the pilot and the observer. Their chances were small, but the light moved on again and upward, and the flying machine was again enveloped in darkness.

Our Young Aeroplane Scouts, however, were destined this night to have another soul-stirring experience, and a closer call even than that threatened by the betraying gleam of the searchlight.

They had a struggle to win a hundred-to-one chance against them, with death as the penalty for failure.

Out over the German lines their engine went dead while they were at a height of perhaps four thousand feet. They dropped a thousand feet and then Billy got his engine working spasmodically. Up they crawled to their former altitude with their nose towards home, and then the engine gave a final gasp and died.

All the probabilities were that they would crash and be smashed to pieces.

There was only one thing which could possibly prevent it, and that was an iron nerve in the pilot's box.

And "iron nerve" was not lacking—that Barry lad was never without it!

He coolly started to coast westwards. On he came until his signal lights showed clearly to the watchers in the aerodrome. It was like the flight of a phantom machine, with its soundless engine.

The Bangor boy got near the aerodrome and then hesitated. He was lost and was coming down rapidly.

He signaled wildly and a score of answering lights flashed back.

He swerved and came swooping down into the aerodrome, saved by a few yards!

All other members of the bombing party were back when the flying twins made their sensational drop, and when they assembled in the commander's quarters to make their reports, it was a different crowd from that laughing, jesting outfit of two hours before. They were pale and haggard, and their eyes were strained and brilliant. No need for them to say what they had been through. Their faces told the story.

One by one they related briefly what they had done. They had, or they had not reached their objective.

When Billy and Henri had their turn, the former, as spokesman, quietly stated:

"We had bad luck, sir."

With Lorry's report of the recent gun-hunting expedition fresh in mind, and several other exploits of supreme daring and nerve-racking nature in which these late additions to his force had been engaged since arrival, the commander, who had been pacing up and down the field like a caged tiger during all the time his boys were over the Boche guns, readily reckoned the almost tragedy veiled by the few words spoken by the gallant young pilot.

This officer himself had spent many bitter days and nights in a fighting plane, and he knew what it meant.

On their way to their billets, Billy and Henri had a chance to ask "Pure Grit" how Bayles and himself had fared as dynamite throwers.

"Jimmy here," confided Patterson, "says we split an aerodrome in two, but I can't swear to it myself, for, believe me, we were going some when the explosion occurred, and the void was blacker than a certain cat we used to own at home. And, say, fellows, I was sure buffaloed when the chief told us that you were on the missing list awhile back. Just wanted to tell you that it gave me heart-burn to think of it."

When "Pure Grit," who had the fixed habit of keeping his feelings under cover, indulged in any sentiment, it could be relied upon that some strong pressure was working inwardly to bring it out.

"No easy sledding yourself, I'll bet," exclaimed Billy, "and you're a bully old boy to think of us!"

Patterson shut up again like a clam and sauntered off to bed, with his helmet down to his nose. Still wearing the bulky garments of flight equipment, in back view the "human hurricane" looked for all the world like an Arctic explorer or a "teddybear."

There was a lull the next day in the field operations, a season of comparative quiet after the tremendous activities of a week or more. Our Young Aeroplane Scouts, having completed a "dead to the world" sleep of some six or seven hours' duration, were in fine fettle and ready to tackle any assignment that might come their way. They started out to seek their friend Lorry, who, as Billy remarked in crossing the grounds, "generally had something up his sleeve" in the way of brisk and risky endeavor. George, however, was not to be found, and inquiry of the mechanics at the aerodrome elicited from one of them a pointing gesture to the east and uplook in the same direction.

"He had a lot of nerve," grumbled the Bangor boy, "to go off and leave us in the land of nod. Wonder what's doing?"

In a little while the boys were able to ascertain

that the Verdun living firebrand was leading in an aviation venture of making it uncomfortable for those engaged in the bringing up of the foe's artillery and food to the front.

The flying twins had their call for similar duty an hour later, when the next bunch of airmen set out to "storm the roads," and not very long thereafter had sight of Lorry's crowd circling in lengthy curves above the highways in enemy territory, occasionally swooping down in lightning charges towards the supply processions, while their machine guns spat a steady stream of livid fire to the accompaniment of that wicked staccato chatter which spells one of the greatest terrors of the front.

Into this bombing and gunning game the reinforcing planes sailed full speed, and that it was not altogether a topside performance was indicated by heavy responsive ground fire, which brought down two of the attacking aviators in a tangle, the crashing of these Ally machines occurring within a hundred yards of the course pursued by Billy and Henri.

The latter pilots were close on the trail of Leader Lorry, when the chief of flight signaled for withdrawal, and that only when the bomb supplies were exhausted.

Down the line five or six miles distant a collection of German Albatrosses were rising, the operators apparently just awakening to the fact that there was need of interference with the further progress of the raiders.

There was enough ammunition left for the Ally machine guns to give the Teuton airmen such a torrid reception that the atmosphere was fairly alive with tumblers and wobbling cripples of the Hun variety.

George, when the "stormers" landed at their own aerodrome, had the satisfaction of reporting "considerable damage to the enemy by the expedition," but his look was downcast when speaking of the loss of Murray and Harrison as the price of the achievement.

"True blue, those boys," he sadly remarked, "and always to be depended upon."

A brief memorial, to be sure, but the tribute was none the less of worth by its brevity.

Not a man in the aerodrome assembly had any assurance of making response at the next roll call!

CHAPTER XIX

STRENUOUS PATROL DUTY

"Just patrol duty for us this morning," Lorry was saying to Our Young Aeroplane Scouts as the trio met at mess the day following the road-rending trip. "If nobody tries to bite us we ought to be back in an hour. This afternoon I'm going to help a fellow up at headquarters in drawing a map, and that's everything in the present program for me."

"Better let Henri here in on the map making," suggested Billy, "he's a whale at that business."

"Sure," instantly agreed George. "Trouville is engaged for the job forthwith."

"When did you establish an employment agency?" laughingly queried the new employee, eyeing his chum.

"When I see talent I always like to encourage it," replied the Bangor boy, with a wink to Lorry.

Thus lightly conversing the three airmen climbed into their machines, along with a half dozen other aviators detailed for the lookover trip, Patterson and Bayles among the number.

The first twenty minutes of flight were without event of consequence. Not a Boche even took the trouble of shooting at the cruisers.

When they had been up a full half-hour, however, their notice was attracted by a column of smoke, apparently not of the gun brand, rising about four miles southward of the flight course.

Lorry, through his glasses, figured the location of the vapor pillar at or in the near vicinity of one of the British observation balloon camps.

Being one of the kind who always wants to know everything there is to know, George instantly wheeled into line of travel that would carry his comrades and himself directly towards the curiosity exciting point.

Going even at an easy aeroplane speed of a mile a minute, the opportunity of close viewing was of quick realization—every aviator in the approaching machines bringing a binocle to bear on the scene.

Another column of smoke greeted the flying contingent when they buzzed into the immediate surroundings, and, also, the cause of the display showing in darting outlines between earth and sky.

Hun air cruisers were shooting down captive gas envelopes, and the smoke was contributed by the burning fabrics.

Two white flecks floating earthward told the airmen that the two passengers of the first balloon had got clear in time. Just then two similar specks appeared suddenly from under another balloon, warning that the Boches were out for a wholesale killing this time. It seemed like a full minute before the aeroplane pilots saw a thin black streak curl up this second balloon, and the volume of smoke increased as the balloon sank, with ever-gathering momentum, down to earth.

Six more white specks now appeared, marking attack on the whole line.

The German Albatross responsible for the second sinking was nearly a half-mile away when Billy Barry, the nearest of the Ally flyers to this catastrophe, went after the hawk like a shot out of a cannon, passing in the onrush a slowly falling object like a large white umbrella—a parachute to which an aeronaut was clinging, his body swaying easily in the breeze.

Before the Bangor boy could get in plugging proximity of the Hun machine, he had reason to shift his course by a sharp wheeling process. He saw in front the Albatross crushing to earth minus a wing, having been hit by a cluster of anti-aircraft shells.

Trouville and Lorry in the meantime had beaten the ground guns in administering strenuous rebuke to another of the flying Fritzs, who had just completed the act of setting a balloon afire, and following up the performance by swooping down on the late occupants of the basket, just getting clear, in parachutes, of the flaming gas bag, the machine gun of the enemy cruiser in full play.

By this hail of lead one of the officers of the wrecked balloon was killed, and, though the other escaped, his parachute was torn by bullets and several of its cords were cut.

But then came the finish of the assailant in the moment of his triumph. Two winged fire-spitters raked the fabric that carried him fore and aft, riddled it like a sieve, man and machine tumbling in shapeless mass to the ground far below.

Pilot Barry swung around from his checked flight, and sweeping westward, saw that two of his aerial company had landed in the middle of a plowed field, and with them a third figure flanked by an outspreading white canopy.

Volplaning to the same field, Billy speedily recognized his own particular pal and Lorry. The other individual was the balloon officer—of whom it could be said, few men have been nearer death and lived to tell the tale.

The Maine lad had it upon his lips to ask as to the whereabouts of the rest of the Ally flyers, especially Patterson and Bayles. Before speaking, however, he read his answer in the great blue dome overhead.

There was a fight going on up there which diverted the attention of the four youths from anything and everything on the ground.

With glasses fixed on high, it could be seen that one of the aerial combatants at the time was plunging into the very thick of the opposing plane array, regardless of all maneuvering rules, and evidently "hitting the line hard," proof of the fact presented to view by a decided separation from even keel of two machines that endeavored to block his way.

"Bet that's 'Pure Grit,'" cried the Bangor boy, "for he's sure a great hand at that sort of thing, always on the smash."

"And getting away with it, as usual," proclaimed Henri, noting another sinking machine along the swathe that the "human hurricane" was cutting.

"The whole 'push' are in it now," commented Lorry, closely following the varying action aloft.

"Got 'em on the run," he soon continued, his voice reaching an exultant high key.

True it was that the participating members of the Ally patrol had then, by their irresistible drive, put the remaining active Huns on the backtrack, and seemingly without serious mishap to any of the first mentioned number.

When the victors ceased pursuit of the vanquished foe, and apparently casting about for sight of their official flight leader, George seized the big parachute umbrella as a signaling device and succeeded in attracting the attention of his now low-flying comrades above.

Like a flock of wild geese seeking a safe feeding place, the mechanical birds descended with discerning caution until they were assured of the lay of the land and the kind of reception they might anticipate.

Once convinced, Lorry in mighty short order had

his whole command on foot and within speaking distance.

Patterson was the first to reach the chief, and showing a blood-streaked face, marked by the red oozing from a gash extending across his forehead, between helmet tip and eyebrows.

"Tried to butt somebody up there, I see," observed the leader, "and made a good job of it, too, I must admit."

"Pure Grit" applied a rather rusty-looking handkerchief to his wound, and drawled reply:

"One Fritz used a revolver on me, I think—a side-swipe. The other kind of gun he had in the boat, with the same kind of aim, I guess, would have taken my whole head off."

"Well, I believe we'll call this a day's work for everybody but Trouville and myself," said Lorry. "Henri and I have a call as map experts when we get back."

The aviators each had a hand-shake with the surviving balloon officer before getting away on the return journey, which, without further trouble, completed what George had announced in advance as "just patrol duty."

CHAPTER XX

SPREAD RED ON THE RHINE

With Lorry and Trouville for the time being on an "inside" job, Barry, Patterson and Bayles were left to their own devices, that is, until about three o'clock in the afternoon. It was something like that hour when occurred a break in the resting period of the three mentioned aviators, and they were volunteers in the movement which put them so soon again in flight.

"Big Bill" Langdon was emerging from his billet in "fighting togs" when sighted by the three members of the "shanty crowd," who were trying to take it easy on rude-rigged benches in front of the mess hall.

Langdon was a Bostonian, a broad-shouldered chap with clear eyes and an engaging smile, and had won the liking of the present observers of his appearance in the open by a cheerful line of talk at all times.

The Massachusetts man was responsible for the jovial statement that "this bombing business isn't war. I am a chauffeur; my car is my plane and my passengers are bombs. I take my passengers over the line and discharge them, safe and sound, and then come home."

Bayles had remarked only the evening before that "Langdon was the only 'duck' who had ever forced 'Pure Grit' to laugh out loud," and for which assertion he had received a prod in the ribs from Patterson.

"Going to take some 'passengers' out in your taxi?" called Jimmy, as "Big Bill" hurried by on his way to the aerodrome.

"A ton of so of 'em," was the smiling reply.

"Let's go and see if we can't pick up an honest quarter by packing somebody's 'grip,'" suggested the irrepressible Bayles to his companions.

The latter took the banter for what it was worth, but inclined to the proposition at least to the extent of following in Langdon's tracks, in order that they might see the outgoing of the "chauffeur."

"Gee," exclaimed Billy, noting the number of flying machines under "tuning" process, "Bill's going to have a lot of competition on his 'car' route to-day!"

The Bangor boy, inspired by the activity of preparation, made it a point to "haunt the elbow" of the commander, and presently putting desire in words by asking the officer if he would consider any more recruits for the expedition then in forming.

By this time Patterson and Bayles had sidled into noticeable position.

The aviation chief gave the aspirants for action the "once over," and queried:

"You've already done your 'bit' for the day, haven't you?"

"Plenty of time to forget it, colonel," responded Billy.

"Get ready, then, and put on speed in doing it," was the crisp order, indicating permission to the eager trio to do extra duty with the squadron shaping for a getaway.

"You'll hear Henri howl, believe me," declared the Maine youth to his companions during the equipment hustle.

"We're going out to help dam a Hun flood," advised Jimmy, who had been using his ears as well as his hands, "and that isn't swearing, either."

Bayles had heard aright—German reinforcements were pouring like a flood down the Oise valley and over the plains of Picardy, and aviation was a means of holding back that threatening flood until the Allies should be also strengthened by additional troops hurrying from every direction.

Among massed airmen the command to which the "shanty crowd" belonged was putting in its quota to harry the advancing columns, a swarm of hornets to be loosed inside the enemy lines with orders to strike hardest where the foe's movement was most dangerous.

In the next half-hour the contingent dispatched to the fray this memorable afternoon were doing their part of the striking with a vengeance—with bursting bombs and the incessant rattle of machine guns.

Bill and Billy—never call them Willie—Langdon and Barry—were somehow drawn together in the destroying maneuvers, and under the roar of their angry motors were roads strewn with the bodies of men and horses and the wreckage of wagons.

For be it known that bombs dropped from aeroplanes are probably the most deadly missiles now in use—more deadly even than big shells, for the steel exterior, being relatively thin, there is plenty of room inside for high explosives. A machine gun from an aeroplane is bad enough, but a well-placed bomb is a massacre.

That is what the "Bills" were doing—"well placing" bombs.

This pair "crossed in" with a number of French bombers over one main highway, and figured in a combined attack on enemy infantry from a height of only twenty yards. It was impossible for the aviators to miss. It was even dangerous for the aeroplanes themselves, as they might well have been upset by their own bombs.

Entire columns were annihilated in this death-dealing charge, and though individually the targets of hundreds of German bullets, Barry and Langdon were among the airmen who came through un-scratched and their machines uninjured.

May have been luck, but more likely that the Hun riflemen were so nerve shaken by the deadly downpour and the daring dashes right into their midst that they could not shoot straight.

Having unloaded in full measure the tearing,

rending projectiles that Langdon had fancifully called "passengers"—indeed every pound of this sort of cargo carried having been disposed of—the "Bills" were upsailing again when they saw a battle-plane of their kind speeding within two or three yards of the ground—going at the rate of about eighty miles an hour, and apparently regardless of the rifle bullets beginning to zip about him, the operator driving direct at a Boche collection march-ing across a field by platoons in columns of fours. The overlooking comrades of the "ground skimmer" noted that the Germans started to run and then, flinging themselves face downward on the ground as the motor roared just above them.

Several never rose again, for the single-charging aviator evidently had a thorough understanding of the use of the machine gun as well as the expert management of an aeroplane under trying circum-stances.

Only extraordinary skill could have kept the op-erator at such a low level from striking something and killing himself.

The Bangor boy mentally guessed right when he thought only of "Pure Grit" Patterson in connection with the remarkable performance he had just witnessed.

When the two "Bills" succeeded in overhauling the redoubtable plunger, who was taking the up-shoot once more, young Barry got near enough to verify his surmise that the chap with the bandaged head at the controlling levers of the trailed plane was the "human hurricane," and the three followed the same line of travel on the return journey.

Lorry and Henri were with the commander when the trio buzzed into the aerodrome, and Trouville wore an expression that was a cross between relief and rebuke.

Langdon no sooner had reported than he was chaffing with another wit of the aviation corps, who had been "tied to the ground" for several days with a bullet-punctured collar bone.

"You look weary, but wealthy, as usual," was the invalid's greeting to "Big Bill."

"Wealthy!" boomed the great voice. "I should say I was. I don't work because I have to. I'm doing this because I like it."

Rather gay for a man who had just been to the very gates of battle inferno and back again!

"This business of bombing," he further remarked,

pulling a pipe out of some inside pocket and filling it, "is all habit. The commander here has a habit of sending us out, and we have a habit of going and bombing the Hun. All a habit, just like smoking, though perhaps not quite so pleasant."

Across the scarred face of "Pure Grit" a wide smile expanded, in tribute to the one man who could force any mirthful exhibit out of him.

His mouth was set in grim lines again when the other "Bill" remarked to the "human hurricane":

"That 'habit' you've got, old top, of ground-sliding alone into whole companies of infantry is up-in-the-pictures stuff, but I'm fearing it isn't at all a lasting occupation."

"The room for you to talk about caution, Billy Barry, isn't bigger than a minute. Come along and let's to the feed trough."

We will go out once more in this volume with Our Young Aeroplane Scouts on an air raid, which extended into Germany—to a point about 150 miles from where the Allied battle line is nearest to the Kaiser's domain.

As a French general had recently observed—"if we cannot break through the enemy's lines—we can leap them."

It was in one of the "leaps" that Billy Barry and Henri Trouville were this time concerned, and very well satisfied to be identified with the aerial squadron assigned to the "awakening" mission.

When the aviation group with which our boys were immediately flying had reached the extreme limit of their flight, the young scouts saw below them a busy Teuton town, with factory chimneys belching forth smoke, crowds thronging the streets and a market apparently in progress.

An attack from aloft was evidently about the last thing in the world the inhabitants were expecting to happen.

Then suddenly from down below many sirens shrieked shrilly, followed by the roar of gunfire, and high up in the clouds shells began to burst all around the plane fleet, as the squadrons closed in over the town. On the ground all was panic and confusion —the people madly hurrying for shelter.

Even as these things were taking place bombs were dropping, and wherever finding billets there were terrifying crashes of falling masonry, with outbursts of flames.

Away to the north of the town tiny specks appeared in the sky, and an easy guess was that they were aeroplanes, but not proving to be enemy cruisers until machines detached from the bombing squadrons spread across the intervening air space to meet the newcomers.

Billy and Henri happened to be in the investigating detail, which, soon discovering that they had Hun flyers with which to deal, opened machine-gun fire in a perfect torrent, and the enemy as promptly returning the fusillade.

The foe, however, appeared to be the first to have enough of it, backtracking, with the Ally airmen in pursuit. One of the German pilots, hard pressed, suddenly turned toward the point where the Bangor boy was flying. The young scout, in anticipation of something of the kind, had already risen to a greater altitude and had his machine gun ready for just such an emergency, firing even while the Boche had his thumbs on his own gun with intent of riddling the young American with bullets.

Not a bullet came the way of the forehanded youngster, though he had expected a shower of lead while in the act himself of firing. Instead, the German had fallen back in his seat, and his machine, out of control, ran so close to the Barry plane as to nearly upset it in the passing.

Billy took another shot at the second man in the wildly careering Hun plane who was trying to get control of it, and with the result that the whole outfit spun round several times and then crashed down to earth, falling, a flaming mass, on the roof of a tall building.

The encounter was so quickly over that Henri, who in the chase after the fleeing Boche planes had overrun the scene of combat a full half mile, found, in swinging about to rejoin his pal, the latter sailing on even keel and as calmly guiding to course as if nothing untoward had happened.

When the bombing squadrons responded to retiring order, having attained all their objectives, they certainly left a red glow on the countryside, and vividly mirrored on the surface flow of the Rhine.

Our Young Aeroplane Scouts had only counted another "day's work."

There are other days, though, in the strenuous lives of Billy Barry and Henri Trouville "Over There." The next volume of the series will keep up with the calendar.